Interactive Student Notebook 1

Chapters 1 – 22

History Alive!®

The UNITED STATES

Teachers' Curriculum Institute

Bert Bower   Jim Lobdell

Managing Editor: Jeri Hayes
Project Editor: Joyce Bartky
Developmental Editor: John Bergez
Editorial Assistant: Anna Embree
Art Director: Tim Stephenson
Production Coordinator: Lynn Sanchez
Graphic Designer: Christy Uyeno
Illustrator: Richard Boles
Photo Editor: Margee Robinson
Operations Manager: Ellen Mapstone

This book is published by Teachers' Curriculum Institute.

 Teachers' Curriculum Institute
PO Box 50996
1170 East Meadow Drive
Palo Alto, CA 94303

Customer Service: (800) 497-6138
www.historyalive.com

ISBN 1-58371-195-3

4 5 6 7 8 9 10 05 04

Contents

Chapter 1 The Native Americans

Preview 1. 1

Reading Notes 1. 2

Processing 1. 6

Chapter 2 European Exploration and Settlement

Preview 2. 7

Reading Notes 2. 8

Processing 2. 13

Chapter 3 The English Colonies in America

Preview 3. 15

Reading Notes 3. 16

Processing 3. 20

Chapter 4 Life in the Colonies

Preview 4. 21

Reading Notes 4. 22

Chapter 5 Toward Independence

Preview 5. 27

Reading Notes 5. 28

Processing 5. 31

Chapter 6 The Declaration of Independence

Preview 6. 33

Reading Notes 6. 34

Activity Notes 6. 36

Chapter 7 The American Revolution

Reading Notes 7. 38

Processing 7. 44

Chapter 8 Creating the Constitution

Preview 8. 45

Reading Notes 8. 46

Processing 8. 50

Chapter 9 The Constitution: A More Perfect Union

Preview 9. 51

Reading Notes 9. 52

Processing 9. 56

Chapter 10 The Bill of Rights

Preview 10 58

Reading Notes 10 60

Activity Notes 10 64

Processing 10 68

Chapter 11 Political Developments in the Early Republic

Preview 11 69

Reading Notes 11 70

Processing 11 73

Chapter 12 Foreign Affairs in the Young Nation

Preview 12 74

Reading Notes 12 76

Processing 12 84

Chapter 13 The Worlds of North and South

Preview 13 85

Reading Notes 13 86

Processing 13 90

Chapter 14 Andrew Jackson and the Growth of American Democracy

Preview 14 91

Reading Notes 14 93

Processing 14 99

Chapter 15 Manifest Destiny and the Growing Nation

Preview 15 101

Reading Notes 15 102

Processing 15 107

Chapter 16 Life in the West

Preview 16 108

Reading Notes 16 110

Processing 16 114

Chapter 17 Mexicano Contributions to the Southwest

Preview 17 115

Reading Notes 17 116

Processing 17 120

Chapter 18 An Era of Reform

Preview 18 122

Reading Notes 18 124

Activity Notes 18 126

Processing 18 130

Chapter 19 African Americans at Mid-Century

Preview 19 131

Reading Notes 19 132

Chapter 20 A Dividing Nation

Preview 20 137

Reading Notes 20 138

Processing 20 142

Chapter 21 The Civil War

Preview 21 145

Reading Notes 21 146

Processing 21 150

Chapter 22 The Reconstruction Era

Preview 22 151

Reading Notes 22 152

Processing 22 157

Directions: Carefully examine the transparency of the Canadian forest. Imagine you have suddenly been placed in this environment, and you must survive there for a year. Describe the shelter you would build, the clothing you would make to protect yourself from the elements, and the tools you would create to acquire food. Tell why you designed the items the way you did. Mention the natural resources you would use.

Directions: 1) Examine the artifacts. 2) Determine the cultural region from which they came. 3) Write the placard letter in the appropriate box. 4) Fill in three environmental features of the region that the artifacts reveal. 5) Read the corresponding section in your book. 6) Write a journal entry for that region. The entry should have four

1.5 Northwest Coast

Placard letter

Features of the Environment:

•

•

•

Journal Entry:

1.6 California

Placard letter

Features of the Environment:

•

•

•

Journal Entry:

NORTHWEST COAST

PLATEAU

GREAT PLAINS

CALIFORNIA

GREAT BASIN

SOUTHWEST

PACIFIC

OCEAN

sentences. It should mention the three artifacts on the placard and three features of the environment. Underline the names of the artifacts and the environmental features.

1.7 Great Basin	Placard letter

Features of the Environment:

•

•

•

Journal Entry:

EASTERN
WOODLANDS

SOUTHEAST

ATLANTIC

OCEAN

1.8 Plateau	Placard letter

Features of the Environment:

•

•

•

Journal Entry:

Directions: 1) Examine the artifacts. 2) Determine the cultural region from which they came. 3) Write the placard letter in the appropriate box. 4) Fill in three environmental features of the region that the artifacts reveal. 5) Read the corresponding section in your book. 6) Write a journal entry for that region. The entry should have four

1.9 Southwest

Placard letter

Features of the Environment:

•

•

•

Journal Entry:

1.10 Great Plains

Placard letter

Features of the Environment:

•

•

•

Journal Entry:

NORTHWEST COAST PLATEAU GREAT PLAINS

CALIFORNIA GREAT BASIN

SOUTHWEST

PACIFIC

OCEAN

Chapter 1: The Native Americans

sentences. It should mention the three artifacts on the placard and three features of the environment. Underline the names of the artifacts and the environmental features.

1.11 Eastern Woodlands

Placard letter

Features of the Environment:

-
-
-

Journal Entry:

EASTERN
WOODLANDS

SOUTHEAST

ATLANTIC

OCEAN

1.12 Southeast

Placard letter

Features of the Environment:

-
-
-

Journal Entry:

Directions: Create an annotated diagram showing the climate, land, and adaptations made by the Native Americans in one cultural region. In your diagram, use words and pictures to describe the land, climate, and adaptations of the Native Americans. A completed diagram for the Northwest Coast region might look like this:

Northwest Coast

Land: Heavily forested, near the sea

Climate: Mild

Adaptations:

• Harpoon for seal hunting

• Bark capes made from cedar trees

• Plank houses made from cedar trees

PREVIEW 2

Labeling Classroom Furniture: Like Claiming Land in the Americas

Classroom Experience	Historical Connection

Directions: Read the section. Then use the words in the Word Bank to answer the questions in each box.

2.2 Spain Starts an Empire

Word Bank: Christopher Columbus, Hernán Cortés, Francisco Pizarro, gold, disease, slave traders

How did Spain establish territorial claims in the Caribbean and South America?	What was life like in Spanish settlements in the Caribbean and South America?

What type of relationship existed between the Spanish and Native Americans living in the Caribbean and South America?

Directions: Read the section. Then use the words in the Word Bank to answer the questions in each box.

2.3 The Spanish Borderlands

Word Bank: Francisco Coronado, Ponce de León, pueblos, presidios, missions, priests

How did Spain establish territorial claims in North America?	What types of permanent settlements did the Spanish establish in North America?

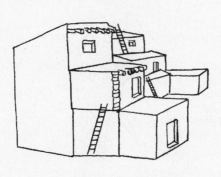

What type of relationship existed between the Spanish and Native Americans living in North America?

READING NOTES 2

Directions: Read the section. Then use the words in the Word Bank to answer the questions in each box.

2.4 New France

Word Bank: Jacques Cartier, Robert de La Salle, coureurs de bois, missionaries, Huron

How did France establish territorial claims in North America?	What was life like in French settlements in North America?

What type of relationship existed between the French and Native Americans living in North America?

READING NOTES 2

Directions: Read the section. Then use the words in the Word Bank to answer the questions in each box.

2.5 Jamestown: The First English Colony

Word Bank: John Cabot, Captain John Smith, Pocahontas, mosquitoes, Starving Time, John Rolfe

How did England establish territorial claims in North America?

What was life like in Jamestown?

What type of relationship existed between the English and the Native Americans living around Jamestown?

Directions: Read the section. Then use the words in the Word Bank to answer the questions in each box.

2.6 New Netherland: The Short-Lived Dutch Settlement

Word Bank: Henry Hudson, Peter Minuit, Peter Stuyvesant, fur trade, Iroquois, English, New York

How did the Netherlands establish territorial claims in North America? .	What was life like in New Netherland?

What type of relationship existed between the Dutch and Native Americans living in New Netherland?

Directions: Create a historical marker that commemorates a settlement established by the English, Dutch, French, or Spanish in the Americas. Your marker should include
• an appropriate title.
• a brief summary that clearly explains 1) how the settlement was established, 2) how Native Americans living near the settlement were treated, 3) how the settlement flourished or failed.
• visuals that illustrate the three main ideas of the summary.
• writing that is free from spelling and grammatical errors.

Directions: Examine the map that your teacher has projected. Then, working with a partner, record answers to the questions below.

1. Identify four details from the map.

2. Into how many regions are the 13 colonies divided?

3. Which region had large tobacco plantations?

4. In which region was fishing important?

5. In which region would you find ironworks?

6. Why do you think many large farms were located in the Southern Colonies?

7. Why do you think so much shipbuilding took place in the New England Colonies?

Directions: Before the Colonial Fair: 1) Read about your colony in the appropriate section of *History Alive! The United States.* 2) Find the section of the Reading Notes for your colony, and use the outline of your colony to create a spoke diagram. Add six spokes. On each spoke, write notes describing a key feature of the colony and a symbol or simple illustration of that feature.

During the Colonial Fair: 1) As you visit each booth, add three spokes to the spoke diagram for that colony. Use

3.3 Massachusetts

Really want to live here

Really don't want to live here

Rank

3.4 Rhode Island

Really want to live here

Really don't want to live here

Rank

information from the presentation to record notes and visuals for key features of the colony on the spokes.
2) Mark the spectrum to indicate how much you would like to settle in the colony.

After the Colonial Fair: 1) Read the section that corresponds to each colony. 2) Add three more spokes to each diagram, each with notes and a visual of a key feature of the colony. 3) Rank the colonies from 1 (best) to 8 (worst). Write your rankings for the colonies in the corresponding boxes.

3.5 Connecticut

Really want to live here

Really don't want to live here

Rank

3.6 New York

Really want to live here

Really don't want to live here

Rank

Directions: Before the Colonial Fair: 1) Read about your colony in the appropriate section of *History Alive! The United States.* 2) Find the section of the Reading Notes for your colony, and use the outline of your colony to create a spoke diagram. Add six spokes. On each spoke, write notes describing a key feature of the colony and a symbol or simple illustration of that feature.

During the Colonial Fair: 1) As you visit each booth, add three spokes to the spoke diagram for that colony. Use

3.7 Pennsylvania

Really want to live here　　　　　　**Really don't want to live here**

Rank

3.8 Maryland

Really want to live here　　　　　　**Really don't want to live here**

Rank

information from the presentation to record notes and visuals for key features of the colony on the spokes.
2) Mark the spectrum to indicate how much you would like to settle in the colony.
After the Colonial Fair: 1) Read the section that corresponds to each colony. 2) Add three more spokes to each diagram, each with notes and a visual of a key feature of the colony. 3) Rank the colonies from 1 (best) to 8 (worst). Write your rankings for the colonies in the corresponding boxes.

3.9 Virginia

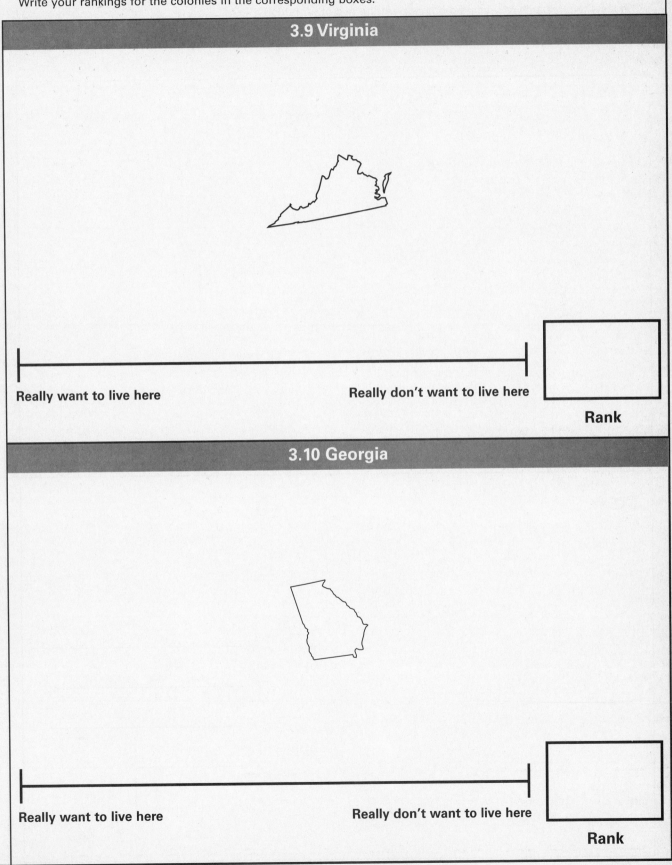

Really want to live here

Really don't want to live here

Rank

3.10 Georgia

Really want to live here

Really don't want to live here

Rank

Directions: Pretend that you are an American colonist in the early 1700s. Write a postcard to a friend in Europe describing the colony you have settled in and your reasons for doing so. Write the message on one side of the postcard, and sketch a picture on the other side. Your postcard must contain

- a proper salutation and closing.
- three reasons you moved to the colony.
- at least two reasons why you did not settle in the two other regions.
- writing that is free of spelling and grammatical errors.
- a colorful image depicting at least one of the colony's best features.

Dear

You are a British newspaper reporter living in London in 1750. You just read an article entitled "Life Is Strange in American Colonies" in the *British Enquirer,* a tabloid newspaper known for inaccurate reporting. You suspect that some of the statements in the story are not true.

Read the following statements from the article. Write "true" next to the statements you think are true, and "false" next to those you think are not true.

_____ 1. Life on a Farm: "Farmers work very little and have a lot of free time."

_____ 2. Life in Cities: "Most colonial cities are built along major waterways and have a variety of jobs and trade."

_____ 3. Rights of Colonists: "People accused of crimes in the colonies are imprisoned without a trial."

_____ 4. Crime and Punishment: "Criminals are rarely punished severely."

_____ 5. Class Differences: "There is remarkable equality of wealth among colonists."

_____ 6. Life for African Americans: "Selling slaves is against the law."

_____ 7. Religion: "Sunday is considered the Lord's Day. Some colonists must devote the day to religious matters."

_____ 8. Education: "Colonial schools do not teach about religion."

_____ 9. Colonial Families: "Colonial parents believe that children should not work and should instead play all day."

_____ 10. Leisure: "Leisure activities often combine work with pleasure."

_____ 11. Food: "Cooking is a time-consuming task."

READING NOTES 4

Directions: After you have examined a placard, read the corresponding section in *History Alive! The United States*. Take notes in the appropriate box. Draw a quick doodle—a simple sketch, diagram, or symbol—to represent the main ideas of the section.

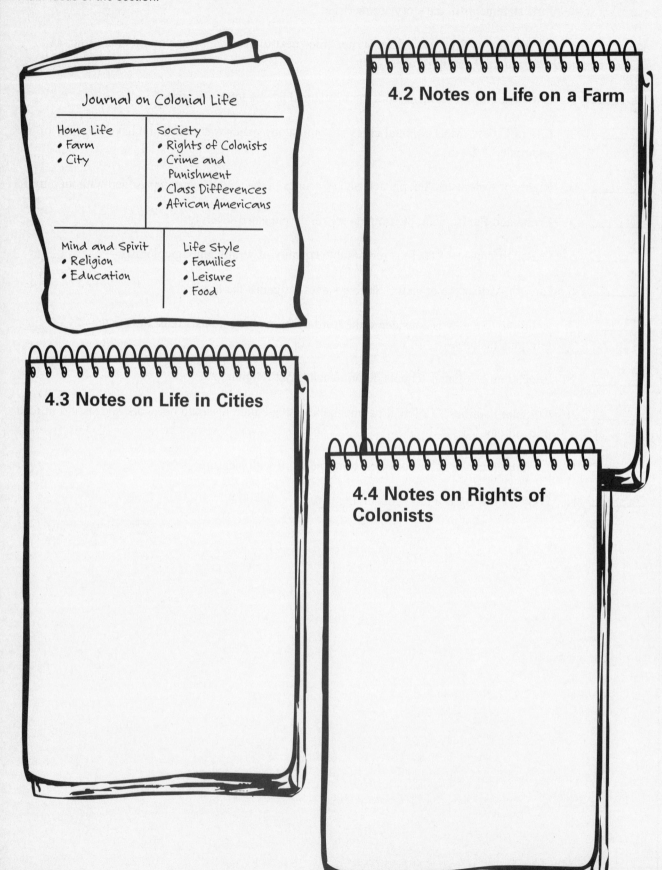

Journal on Colonial Life

Home Life • Farm • City	Society • Rights of Colonists • Crime and Punishment • Class Differences • African Americans
Mind and Spirit • Religion • Education	Life Style • Families • Leisure • Food

4.2 Notes on Life on a Farm

4.3 Notes on Life in Cities

4.4 Notes on Rights of Colonists

4.5 Notes on Crime and Punishment

4.6 Notes on Class Differences

4.7 Notes on Life for African Americans

READING NOTES 4

Directions: After you have examined a placard, read the corresponding section in *History Alive! The United States*. Take notes in the appropriate box. Draw a quick doodle—a simple sketch, diagram, or symbol—to represent the main ideas of the section.

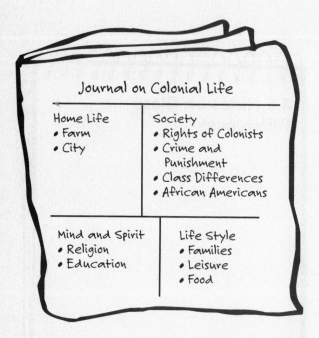

Journal on Colonial Life

Home Life	Society
• Farm	• Rights of Colonists
• City	• Crime and Punishment
	• Class Differences
	• African Americans

Mind and Spirit	Life Style
• Religion	• Families
• Education	• Leisure
	• Food

Section 4.8 Notes on Religion

Section 4.9 Notes on Education

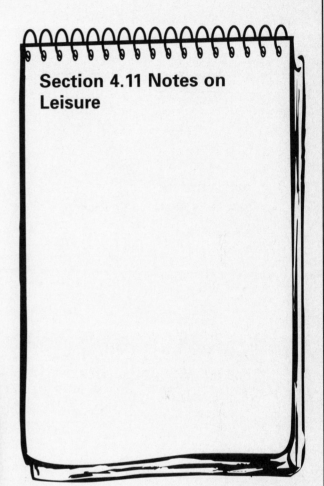

Section 4.10 Notes on Colonial Families

Section 4.11 Notes on Leisure

Section 4.12 Notes on Food

Paying for Photocopies: Like Taxation without Representation

Classroom Experience	Historical Event

READING NOTES 5

Directions: Read Sections 5.2 through 5.8 in *History Alive! The United States*. After you read each section, complete the notes comparing the illustration with the historical events.

5.2 Before 1763

	In Metaphor	In History
	Students happily playing basketball	
	Student Council Minutes	
	No adults allowed	
	Principal's office away from gym	

5.3 Early British Actions

	In Metaphor	In History
	New Rules	
	Half-court only	
	Pay to use	
	Student funds will pay supervisors	
	Student's anger	

Directions: Read Sections 5.2 through 5.8 in *History Alive! The United States.* After you read each section, complete the notes comparing the illustration with the historical events.

5.4 The Townshend Acts

In Metaphor	In History
Man staffing the stand	
Sign reading "Equipment Rental"	
Male student telling friends not to use basketballs	
Female student walking away	

5.5 The Boston Massacre

In Metaphor	In History
Vice principal and security guard	
Protesting students	
Vice principal's threat to suspend	

Directions: Read Sections 5.2 through 5.8 in *History Alive! The United States*. After you read each section, complete the notes comparing the illustration with the historical events.

5.6 The Boston Tea Party

In Metaphor	In History
Sign reading "Cafeteria food only"	
Male student throwing lunch into trash	
Male student cheering in the background	

5.7 The Intolerable Acts

In Metaphor	In History
Students given detention	
Female student angry at male student	
Protest letters	

5.8 Lexington and Concord

In Metaphor	In History
Principal	
Principal's statement	
Running female student	

Directions: Write a dialogue between a Loyalist and a Patriot on whether the colonies should declare independence from Britain. Your dialogue must:

- Begin with these three lines:
  Loyalist: I can't understand why you want the colonies to break away from the British Empire. It's just not a smart idea.
  Patriot: Not a smart idea? I'll tell you why it's a smart idea.
  Loyalist: Okay, but you need to hear my side of it, too...

- Contain at least three key reasons why Patriots support independence.
- Contain at least three key reasons why Loyalists oppose independence.
- Use language that reflects the passionate feelings held by Loyalists and Patriots on the topic of independence.
- Be free from spelling and grammatical errors.

Directions: In a short paragraph, explain the phrase "It was the last straw." Describe a situation in which this statement was true for you.

_____

_____

_____

_____

_____

_____

_____

_____

_____

_____

_____

_____

_____

_____

_____

_____

_____

_____

_____

_____

_____

_____

_____

_____

_____

_____

_____

_____

_____

Directions: 1) Read Sections 6.2 – 6.6 in *History Alive! The United States.* 2) Label Britain and the 13 colonies in the illustration below. 3) In the small inset box at the end of each strand of the unraveling rope, draw a symbol to represent the event described in the corresponding section. 4) In the large box, complete this sentence: _____ *weakened the ties between the colonies and Britain because....* 5) After you complete a symbol and an explanation, have your teacher check your work. The first strand has been partially completed for you.

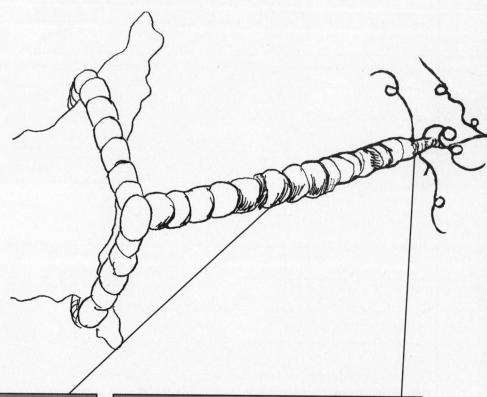

6.2 The War Begins	6.3 The Siege of Boston
The Battle of Bunker Hill weakened the ties between the colonies and Britain because…	

6.4 Toward Independence

6.5 Thomas Jefferson Drafts a Declaration

6.6 The Final Break

Directions: 1) Read the excerpt. 2) Rephrase the excerpt into simple language a third grader could understand. 3) Draw a simple illustration to represent the excerpt. 4) Have your teacher check your work. Repeat these steps for all excerpts.

Excerpt	Rephrased Excerpt	Simple Sketch
Excerpt 1: "When in the Course of human events it becomes necessary for one people to dissolve the political bands which have connected them with another and to assume among the powers of the earth, the separate and equal station to which the Laws of Nature and of Nature's God entitle them, a decent respect to the opinions of mankind requires that they should declare the causes which impel them to the separation."		
Excerpt 2: "We hold these truths to be self-evident, that all men are created equal, that they are endowed by their Creator with certain unalienable Rights, that among these are Life, Liberty and the pursuit of Happiness."		
Excerpt 3: "That to secure these rights, Governments are instituted among Men, deriving their just powers from the consent of the governed."		
Excerpt 4: "That whenever any Form of Government becomes destructive of these ends, it is the Right of the People to alter or to abolish it, and to institute new Government."		

Excerpt	Rephrased Excerpt	Simple Sketch
Excerpt 5: "The history of the present King of Great Britain is a history of repeated injuries and usurpations, all having in direct object the establishment of an absolute Tyranny over these States."		
Excerpt 6: "To prove this [that England has interfered with colonial rights], let Facts be submitted to a candid world. He has refused his Assent to Laws, the most wholesome and necessary for the public good."		
Excerpt 7: "In every stage of these Oppressions We have Petitioned for Redress in the most humble terms: Our repeated Petitions have been answered only by repeated injury. A Prince, whose character is thus marked by every act which may define a Tyrant, is unfit to be the ruler of a free people."		
Excerpt 8: "We, therefore… solemnly publish and declare, That these United Colonies are, and of Right ought to be Free and Independent States."		

7.2: American Strengths and Weaknesses

Read Section 7.2 and follow the directions below.

List three weaknesses of the Americans at the start of the war.
1.
2.
3.

Besides patriotism, list two American strengths at the start of the war.
1.
2.

7.3 British Strengths and Weaknesses

Read Section 7.3 and follow the directions below.

List three strengths of the British at the start of the war.
1.
2.
3.

List two weaknesses of the British at the start of the war.
1.
2.

Complete the annotations for the map of Round 1 of Capture the Flag.

The Blue team is smaller. It has not warmed up. It hasn't played Capture the Flag as much as the Red team, just like...

The Red team is larger. It has warmed up. It has played Capture the Flag more than the Blue team, just like...

The Blue team's captain has experience playing Capture the Flag, just like...

The White team cheers for the Blue team, just like...

Half of the Red team starts the game far away from the field, just like...

7.4: Britain Almost Wins the War

Read Section 7.4 and answer the questions below.

Why did the Declaration of Independence increase Americans' motivation to fight and win the war?

For which group of Americans did the Declaration of Independence raise hopes as well as questions? Why?

What factors allowed the British to almost win the war in 1776?

Complete the annotations for the map of Round 2 of Capture the Flag.

The teacher tells the Blue team that they will receive a prize if they win the game. This increases their motivation to win, just like…

Because they have more experienced players, the Red team is almost able to steal the Blue flag, just like…

One member of the Blue team is told that he or she might not receive the prize, even if the Blue team wins. That player must decide whether to stay on the Blue team or switch to the Red team, just like…

7.5: A Pep Talk and Surprise Victories
Read Section 7.5 and answer the questions below.

In your own words, what was the message of Thomas Paine's pamphlet *The Crisis*?

How were the Americans able to win such an overwhelming victory at Trenton?

How did victories at Trenton and Princeton affect American morale?

Complete the annotations for the map of Round 3 of Capture the Flag.

The teacher gives the Blue team a pep talk and encourages them to keep fighting, just like…

The teacher adds a second Blue flag. This makes it harder for the Red team to win and boosts the morale of the Blue team, just like…

7.6: The Tide Begins to Turn
Read Section 7.6 and answer the questions below.

As the war progressed, how did Washington revise his military strategy?

Why did the American cause look more hopeful after the Battle of Saratoga?

Name two foreigners who were present with the Americans at Valley Forge, and explain how they helped the Americans.

1.

2.

Complete the annotations for the map of Round 4 of Capture the Flag.

The teacher tells the Blue team that they do not have to capture the Red flag to win. Instead, they must keep the Red team from capturing all the Blue flags, just like…

The teacher has one volunteer from the White team join the Blue team, just like…

The teacher tells the Blue team that if they can hold on for one more round, they may receive help, just like…

7.7: The War Goes South
Read Section 7.7 and answer the questions below.

What tactics did the Americans use successfully against the British in the Southern Colonies?

How did the success of the Continental Army in the South contribute to the American victory?

How did the French help the Americans in the Battle of Yorktown?

Complete the annotations for the map of Round 5 of Capture the Flag.

The teacher adds a third Blue flag. This makes it harder for the Red team to win, just like…

The White team enters into the game to help the Blue team in this round, just like…

7.8: The War Ends

Read Section 7.8 and answer the questions below.

How did the British people respond to news of the Battle of Yorktown?

What were three key provisions of the Treaty of Paris?

1.

2.

3.

Complete the annotations for the map of the end of the Capture the Flag game.

By the end of Round 6, many members of the Red team don't want to play anymore, but some do, just like…

Blue Flags

We won!

At the end of the game, the Blue, White, and Red team captains shake hands. The Blue and White teams receive their prizes. The Red team captain hands over the Red flag. The Blue team promises to be nice to the Red team, just like…

Create a Fourth of July parade banner that commemorates the reasons the Continental Army was able to defeat the British in the Revolutionary War. Complete these steps:

1. Create a slogan for your banner in large letters. For example, your slogan might say: "David Defeats Goliath: How We Won Our Independence."

2. Decorate the banner with at least five simple visual symbols that represent different reasons the Americans won the Revolutionary War. For example, you might draw the French flag to represent the French assistance that helped the Americans win.

3. Beneath the banner, write of a three- or four-word caption that explains what each symbol represents. For example, as a caption for the French flag, you might write, "Help from French Allies."

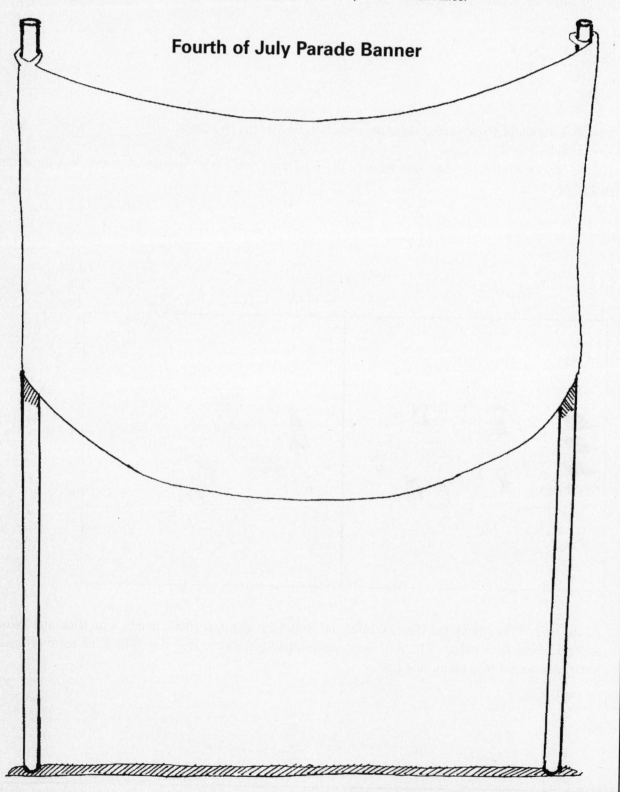

Fourth of July Parade Banner

PREVIEW 8

Experiencing the Weaknesses of the Articles of Confederation

Classroom Experience	Articles of Confederation

Directions: Read each section in *History Alive! The United States.* Then answer the question in the corresponding box.

8.3 Shays's Rebellion and the Need for Change

Why were many Americans concerned by the actions of Shays and his supporters?

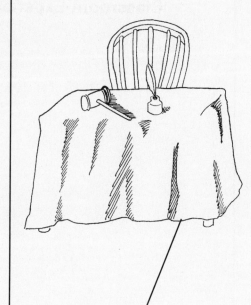

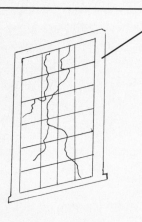

8.4 Opening the Constitutional Convention

Describe the background of the delegates.

8.5 Issue: How Should States Be Represented in the New Government?

How did the Virginia Plan and the New Jersey Plan differ?

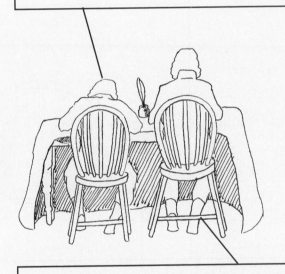

8.6 Resolution: The Great Compromise

What compromise did the delegates create to resolve the issue of state representation?

Directions: Read each section in *History Alive! The United States.* Then answer the question in the corresponding box.

8.7 Issue: How Should Slaves Be Counted?

How did the views of delegates from northern states differ from those of delegates from southern states on this issue?

8.8 Resolution: The Three-Fifths Compromise

What compromise did the delegates create to resolve this issue?

8.9 Issue: How Should the Chief Executive Be Elected?

Why didn't the delegates agree on how the national executive should be chosen?

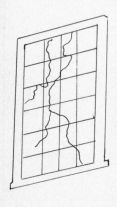

8.10 Resolution: The Electoral College

What compromise did the delegates create to resolve this issue?

8.11 The Convention Ends

Why did some delegates refuse to sign the final draft of the Constitution?

8.12 The Constitution Goes to the Nation

What were *The Federalist Papers*, and why were they written?

Directions: Create a poster that might have been used to encourage people to support ratification of the Constitution. Your poster must include

- a catchy slogan.
- three reasons why states should ratify the Constitution.
- a visual to accompany each reason.
- extra creative touches to make your poster visually appealing, such as a decorative border.
- writing that is free from spelling and grammatical errors.

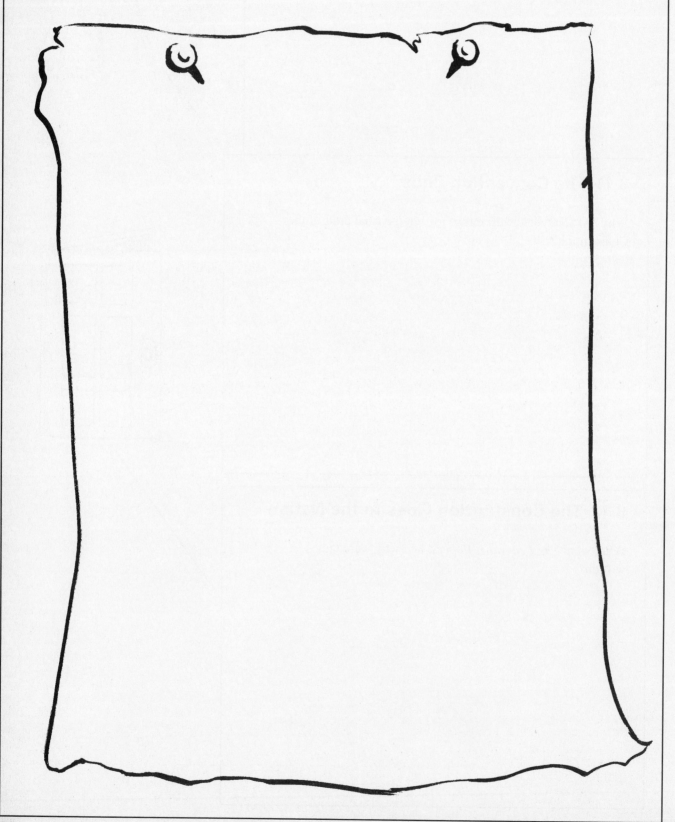

Directions: Think about some law with which you disagree. This might be a curfew law, a law that limits working hours for teenagers, a law limiting skateboard riding, or the like. Explain why you disagree with the law. To whom do you think you would go to have this law changed? Be prepared to share your answer with the class.

To Whom Do I Complain?

READING NOTES 9

Directions: 1. Read Sections 9.3 through 9.7. 2. Complete the plaques on the office walls. 3. Attach each headline from Student Handout 9 a newspaper in the office of the official who has the power to take that action. Powers for

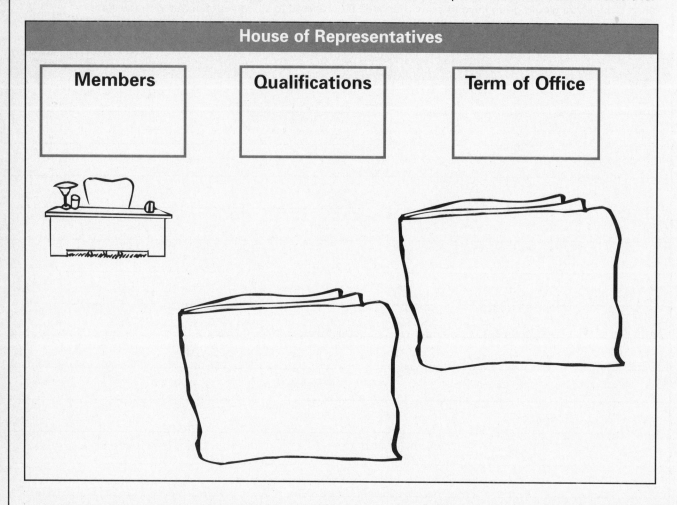

House of Representatives

Members

Qualifications

Term of Office

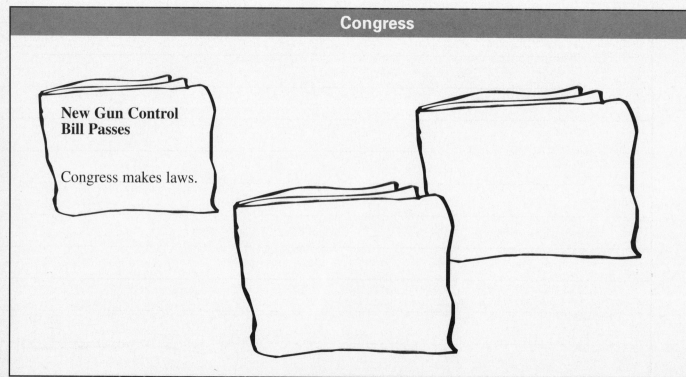

Congress

New Gun Control
Bill Passes

Congress makes laws.

READING NOTES 9

each official are found in more than one section of your book. 4. Below the headline, write the power that brought about this action. One example has been done for you.

Senate

Members

Qualifications

Term of Office

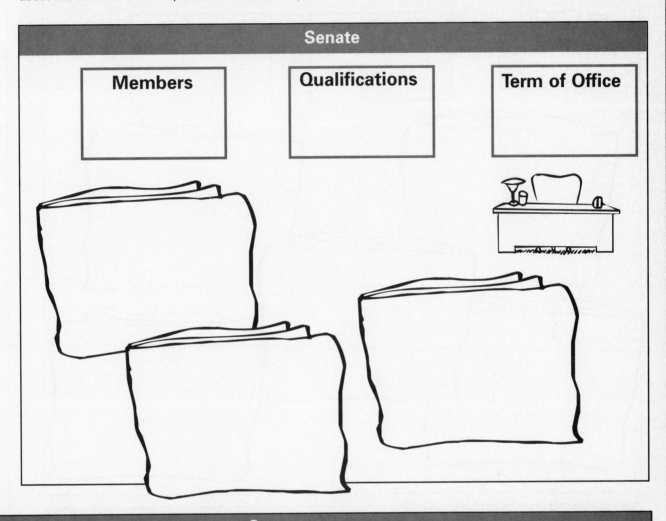

Congress

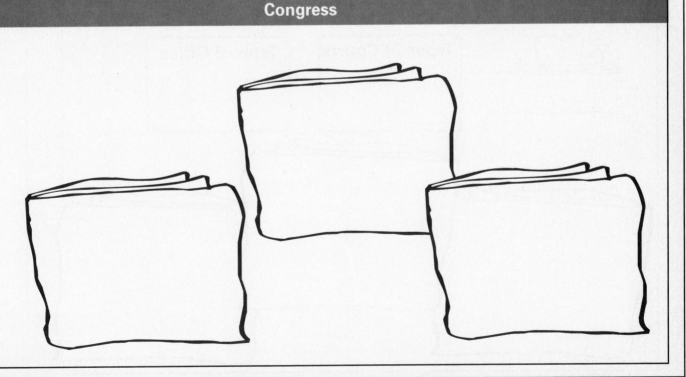

The Executive Branch

Members	Term of Office

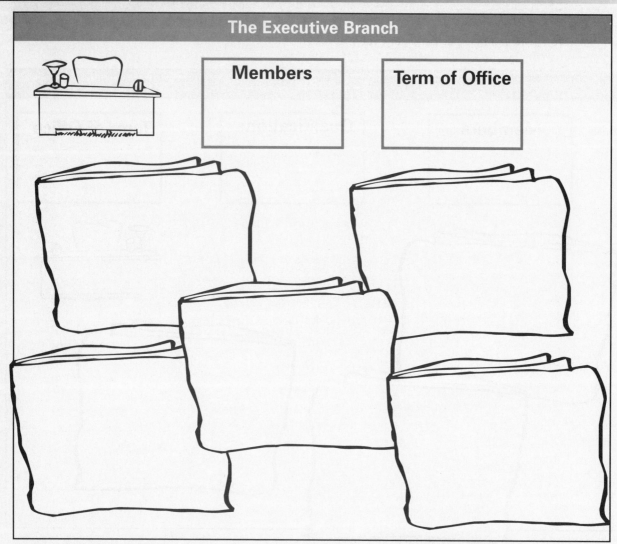

The Judicial Branch

Types of Courts	Term of Office

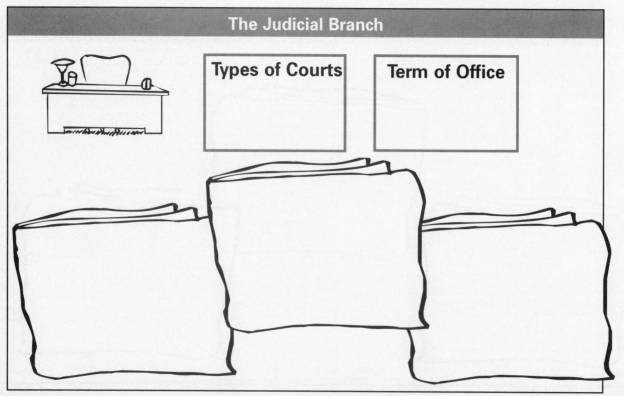

Directions: Read Section 9.8. In the top part of the upper circle, list the powers of the federal government. In the bottom part of the lower circle, list the powers of the state governments. In the area where the two circles intersect, list the powers shared by the state and federal governments.

Federalism

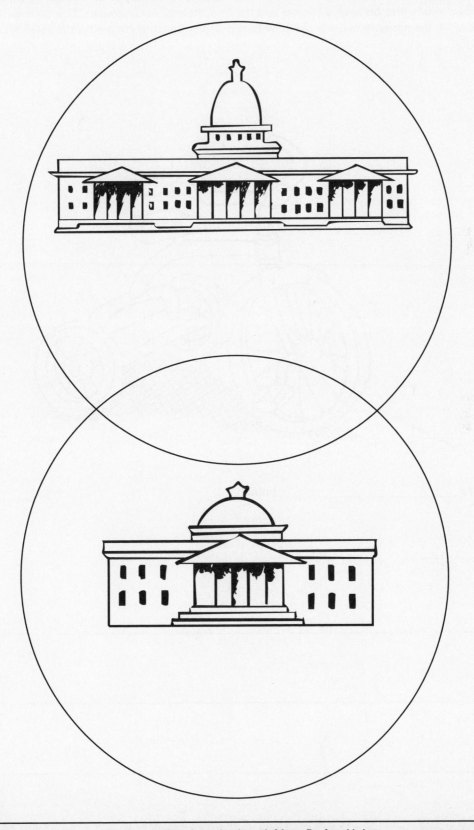

Directions: In this assignment, you will compare the Constitution to a tricycle. To complete this comparison, or metaphor, follow these steps:

1. Write this caption below the illustration: "The three branches of government under the Constitution can be compared to a tricycle."

2. Label the metaphor using at least eight of the following terms: *Constitution, The People, Executive Branch, Legislative Branch, Judicial Branch, President, Congress, Supreme Court, Checks and Balances, Separation of Powers.* One label has been partially completed. You may add to the picture if you like.

3. Complete three statements beginning with "The Constitution is like a tricycle BECAUSE" to explain the three most important similarities between a tricycle and the Constitution. For example, "The Constitution is like a tricycle BECAUSE the handlebars guide the wheels, just as the Constitution guides the three branches of government."

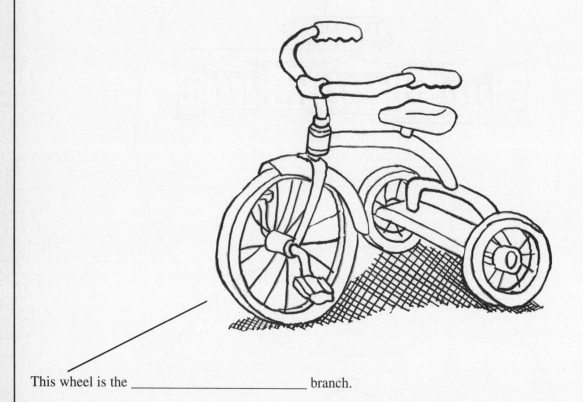

This wheel is the _____ branch.

The Constitution is like a tricycle BECAUSE

1 _____

2 _____

3 _____

Directions: Follow along as your teacher reads the Parents' Constitution aloud. Then discuss the questions with your partner and record answers. Be prepared to share your answers.

Parents' Constitution

WE, THE PARENTS OF THE UNITED STATES, IN ORDER TO FORM MORE PERFECT FAMILIES, RAISE OBEDIENT CHILDREN, ENSURE DOMESTIC TRANQUILITY, PROVIDE FOR OUR CHILDREN'S DEFENSE, PROMOTE THE GENERAL WELFARE, AND SECURE THE BLESSINGS OF LIBERTY TO OURSELVES AND OUR CHILDREN, DO ORDAIN AND ESTABLISH THIS PARENTS' CONSTITUTION FOR THE UNITED STATES OF AMERICA.

I. Parents shall have the power to command complete respect from their children.

II. Parents shall have the power to assign chores to their children and to punish children when the chores are not done properly.

III. Parents shall have the power to promote family togetherness even if this power interferes with their children's social lives.

IV. Parents shall have the power to ask their children questions and to expect honest answers.

V. Parents shall have the power to make all decisions about family spending, including the power to restrict children's spending on unproductive or harmful items.

VI. Parents shall have the power to decide how much time their children's friends can spend with their child.

1. Do you believe parents should have all of the powers described in the Parents' Constitution? If not, which ones would you restrict?

2. How would you change the Parents' Constitution to make it fairer for children?

3. What rights should children have to protect them from the powers of parents? List at least five rights that you and your partner believe are important.

Directions: Read Sections 10.3 through 10.6 in *History Alive! The United States*. For each section, examine the illustrations on the wall drawing and decide which block(s) represents the amendments you read about. Write the

number of the corresponding amendment in each block, and record notes about the rights each illustration represents.

Directions: Read Sections 10.3 through 10.6 in *History Alive! The United States*. For each section, examine the illustrations on the wall drawing, and decide which block(s) represents the amendments you read about. Write the

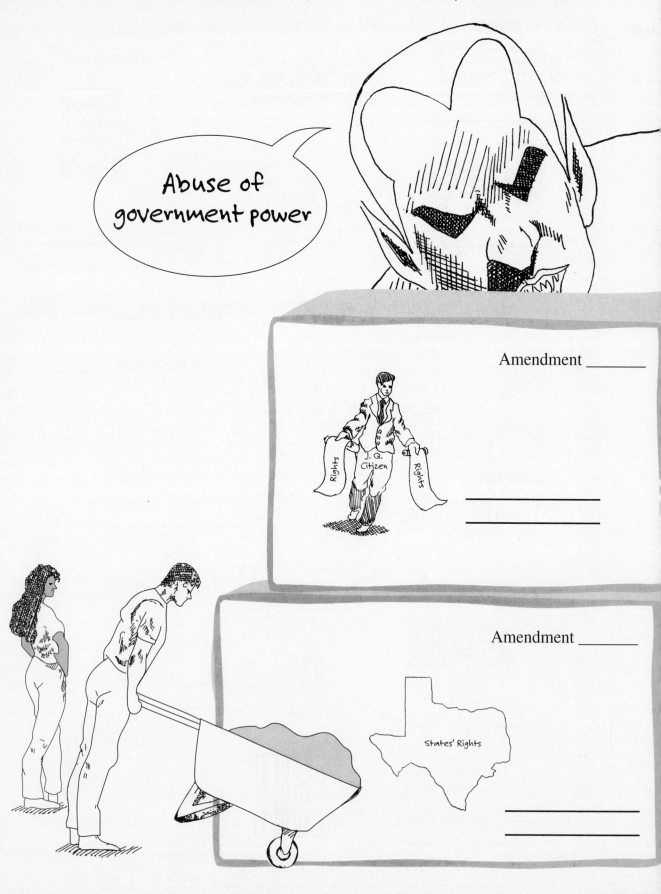

number of the corresponding amendment in each block, and record notes about the rights each illustration represents.

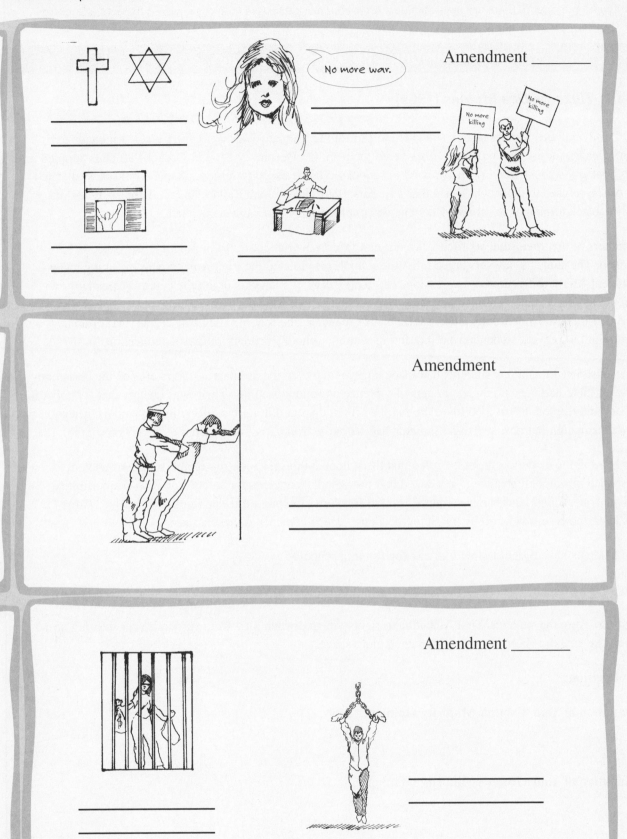

Directions: For each Supreme Court case, have one student in your group read the case aloud. Next, discuss the issues the Supreme Court considered. Vote on the question involved in the case. Record your vote and explain the majority and minority (if there are any) opinions. After your class discusses the case, record the actual Supreme Court decision.

Debating Supreme Court Cases

Case 1: *Tinker v. Des Moines* (1969)

In 1965, several Des Moines students decided to protest the Vietnam War by wearing black armbands to school. Des Moines school principals discovered the plan. On December 14, 1965, school officials adopted a policy that any student wearing an armband to school would be asked to remove it, and would be suspended if he or she refused to do so. On December 16, Mary Beth Tinker, John Tinker, and Christopher Eckhardt wore the black armbands to school. They knew about the policy and were suspended.

The fathers of the three students filed a lawsuit in a federal district court, asking that the suspensions be cancelled. The students' lawyers argued that the school had violated the First Amendment by taking away the students' right to freedom of expression. The school district's lawyers urged the court to consider how controversial the Vietnam conflict was. They argued that school officials had made the policy because they feared that the armbands would cause a serious disturbance at the school. They also argued that officials had the right to prevent students from interfering with the school's primary purpose—education.

Evidence showed that a few students had made angry remarks to the armband wearers outside the classroom. However, there had been no threats or acts of violence on school grounds. There was no sign that schoolwork had been interrupted. It was also revealed that the school district did not ban all political symbols. They allowed campaign buttons, and some students had worn the Iron Cross, considered to be a Nazi symbol.

After hearing the evidence, the court ruled that the school authorities took reasonable action to prevent disturbance of school discipline. They stated that the schools' concerns for safety, and their responsibility to all students, limited individual students' right to freedom of expression. The families appealed. Three years later, the case was heard by the Supreme Court, which considered these issues:

1. Do students have a right to freedom of expression in school?

2. Do school officials have the right to limit freedom of expression?

Question: Were the students' First Amendment rights violated when they were suspended for wearing armbands? Use an extra sheet of paper if you need more space.

Your Decision:

Explanation of Your Group's Majority Opinion:

Explanation of Your Group's Minority Opinion:

Actual Supreme Court Ruling:

Directions: For each Supreme Court case, have one student in your group read the case aloud. Next, discuss the issues the Supreme Court considered. Vote on the question involved in the case. Record your vote and explain the majority and minority (if there are any) opinions. After your class discusses the case, record the actual Supreme Court decision.

Debating Supreme Court Cases

Case 2: *Hazelwood School District v. Kuhlmeier* (1988)

In 1988, a Missouri high school principal removed two pages of the school's six-page newspaper without telling the student editors. The pages had personal stories of teenagers at the school. In one article, a student had written about divorce and had brutally criticized her father. The other article was about teenage pregnancy, and described experiences with sex and birth control. The principal was concerned that in the first article the father had not been given a chance to respond. In the second article, he thought that the references to sexual activity were inappropriate for younger students. He also worried that the article might violate the privacy of the students described in it.

Cathy Kuhlmeier and other editors of *Spectrum*, the school newspaper, filed a lawsuit against the school district. They claimed that the principal's actions were censorship, and violated their First Amendment right to freedom of press. The lawyers for the student editors argued that the principal should only be allowed to omit articles that would disrupt the school. They said that these articles would not have caused any disruption. Lawyers for the school district responded that the district paid for most of the production cost of the newspaper. Therefore, they argued, the district was the publisher and had the final say on the content of the paper, just as publishers control adult newspapers. They pointed out that the principal had not limited students' private expression. He had made no attempt to stop the students from later photocopying the omitted articles and distributing them on campus.

A federal appeals court sided with the students, agreeing that their First Amendment rights had been violated. Hazelwood School District appealed to the Supreme Court, which considered these issues:

1. Who is considered the publisher of a school newspaper, with the right to determine the content of the paper?

2. Under what circumstances, if any, does the First Amendment allow school officials the right to censor school newspapers?

Question: Did the principal violate the students' First Amendment right to freedom of press by censoring their newspaper? Use an extra sheet of paper if you need more space.

Your Decision:

Explanation of Your Group's Majority Opinion:

Explanation of Your Group's Minority Opinion:

Actual Supreme Court Ruling:

ACTIVITY NOTES 10

Directions: For each Supreme Court case, have one student in your group read the case aloud. Next, discuss the issues the Supreme Court considered. Vote on the question involved in the case. Record your vote and explain the majority and minority (if there are any) opinions. After your class discusses the case, record the actual Supreme Court decision.

Debating Supreme Court Cases

Case 3: *Wallace v. Jafree* (1985)

In 1982, a lawyer named Ishmael Jafree discovered that his five-year-old son was being asked to recite prayers in his Alabama public school class. Jafree felt that this violated the Constitution's "separation of Church and State" clause, as well as his son's First Amendment right to freedom of religion. At the time, Alabama law authorized one minute of silence in all public schools "for meditation or voluntary prayer." Jafree filed a lawsuit in the federal district court to strike down the law.

Alabama state lawyers argued that the law called only for a "moment of silence," and did not require a child to pray to a particular God or to pray at all. Jafree's lawyers argued that the law intended to establish religion in the schools. Thus, they argued, it clearly violated the First Amendment. In addition, the lawyers pointed out that the children had been taught specific prayers, including "The Lord's Prayer" and "God is Great, God is Good." In some cases, students had been asked to recite the prayers in place of a moment of silence. If children refused to participate, other students teased them. Therefore, Jafree's lawyers argued, the law was not being followed as it was written.

The federal district court decided in favor of the state, saying that states had a right to establish an official religion. The United States Court of Appeals overturned the decision, saying that the teacher's activities violated the First Amendment. The court also stated that the law in Alabama encouraged religious activities. The State of Alabama appealed the case to the Supreme Court, which considered these issues:

1. Was the law authorizing a moment of silence for meditation or voluntary prayer an attempt to establish a religion?

2. Is a child's First Amendment right to freedom of religion violated if voluntary prayer is allowed in the school?

Questions: Did the Alabama law violate the First Amendment clause that prohibits the government from establishing a religion? Did the law violate the child's First Amendment right to freedom of religion? Use an extra sheet of paper if you need more space.

Your Decision:

Explanation of Your Group's Majority Opinion:

Explanation of Your Group's Minority Opinion:

Actual Supreme Court Ruling:

ACTIVITY NOTES 10

Directions: For each Supreme Court case, have one student in your group read the case aloud. Next, discuss the issues the Supreme Court considered. Vote on the question involved in the case. Record your vote and explain the majority and minority (if there are any) opinions. After your class discusses the case, record the actual Supreme Court decision.

Debating Supreme Court Cases

Case 4: *New Jersey v. T.L.O.* (1985)

In 1980, T.L.O., a 14-year-old freshman at a New Jersey high school, was caught smoking in the bathroom. T.L.O. told the vice principal she had not been smoking and claimed she did not smoke at all. The vice principal then searched her purse. He found not only cigarettes, but rolling papers, a small amount of marijuana, a pipe, a large amount of cash, and a list of student names and amounts of money owed to T.L.O. The school gave this evidence to the juvenile court, which prosecuted T.L.O. for drug dealing.

T.L.O.'s lawyers argued that the vice principal had violated the Fourth Amendment, which protects citizens against unreasonable search and seizure. They said that the evidence should be thrown out because it was obtained illegally. The juvenile court refused to throw out the evidence. The court ruled that school officials could search students if they had reasonable suspicion that a student was doing something illegal or against school rules. They stated that the vice principal's suspicion that T.L.O. had been smoking justified his decision to open her purse. Once the purse was open and he discovered rolling papers, his reasonable suspicion that she was carrying marijuana justified a further search. The court convicted T.L.O. of drug dealing.

T.L.O. appealed the juvenile court's decision to the New Jersey Supreme Court. This court disagreed that the vice principal had reasonable grounds to search T.L.O.'s purse. According to the court, the crime T.L.O. was accused of—smoking—was not related to what was in her purse. Smoking on campus violated school rules, but possession of cigarettes was not against the rules. The court stated that the vice principal's belief that T.L.O. was lying was not enough to justify the search of her purse. Finally, even if he had been justified in opening the purse, the evidence he saw of drug use did not justify the extensive search of her things. The New Jersey court overturned the juvenile court ruling. This case came before the U.S. Supreme Court, which considered these issues:

1. Does the Fourth Amendment protect students from searches by school officials?

2. Under what circumstances, if any, can school officials search students or their belongings?

Question: Was the search of T.L.O.'s purse illegal? Use an extra sheet of paper if you need more space.

Your Decision:

Explanation of Your Group's Majority Opinion:

Explanation of Your Group's Minority Opinion:

Actual Supreme Court Ruling:

Directions: Create a comic strip that tells a story about how difficult life might be today in your community if there were no Bill of Rights. Your comic strip must

- have at least six panels.
- use your town or neighborhood as its setting.
- use middle school students as characters (as well as others if you want).
- contain a conflict that focuses on the violation of at least three rights protected by the Bill of Rights.
- contain a fitting resolution to the conflict.
- be colorful, legible, and neat.

Listen to the CD selections, "Hail, Columbia" and "Fair and Free Elections." For each song, answer the questions below.

"Hail, Columbia"

1. What is the mood of this piece?

_____

_____

_____

_____

_____

2. Why do you think this song was written?

_____

_____

_____

_____

_____

"Fair and Free Elections"

1. What is the mood of this piece?

_____

_____

_____

_____

_____

2. Why do you think this song was written?

_____

_____

_____

_____

_____

Directions: Read Section 11.4. Record notes for each subhead. Then, within the small box, draw an icon representing an important point in your notes.

11.4 Alexander Hamilton

Personal Background

Best Form of Government

Ideal Economy

View of Human Nature

Relations with Britain and France

Directions: Read Section 11.5. Record notes for each subhead. Then, within the small box, draw an icon representing an important point in your notes.

11.5 Thomas Jefferson

Personal Background

Best Form of Government

Ideal Economy

View of Human Nature

Relations with Britain and France

Directions: Read Section 11.6, and list Hamilton's and Jefferson's views on political issues that emerged during John Adams' presidency.

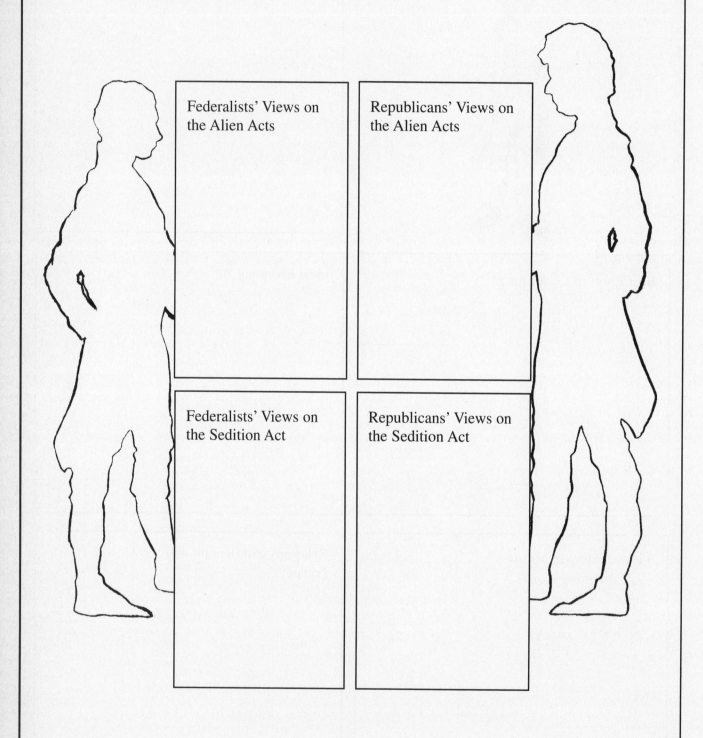

Federalists' Views on
the Alien Acts

Republicans' Views on
the Alien Acts

Federalists' Views on
the Sedition Act

Republicans' Views on
the Sedition Act

Directions: Imagine that you are responsible for creating a television commercial to represent the political ideas of either the Federalists or the Republicans. Create a storyboard to illustrate what would appear on the television screen at four different points in the commercial. Below each illustration, explain your drawing. Your storyboard should

- clearly represent important political ideas held by either the Federalists or the Republicans.
- contain at least one reason a Federalist or a Republican should be elected in 1800.
- use language that reflects the passionate feelings held by Federalists or Republicans.
- be free of spelling and grammatical errors.

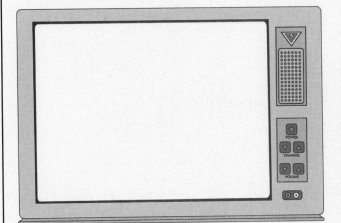
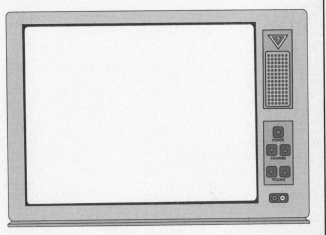

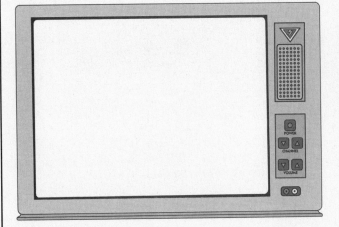
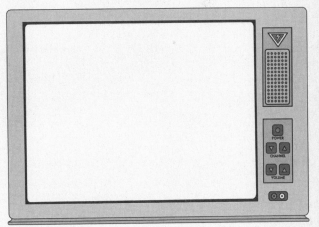

PREVIEW 12

Directions: Examine the map your teacher has projected. Write the names of the countries that have claims in North America in the appropriate places on the map below. Then, working with a partner, discuss and record answers to the questions on the following page.

Examining Claims in North America in 1796

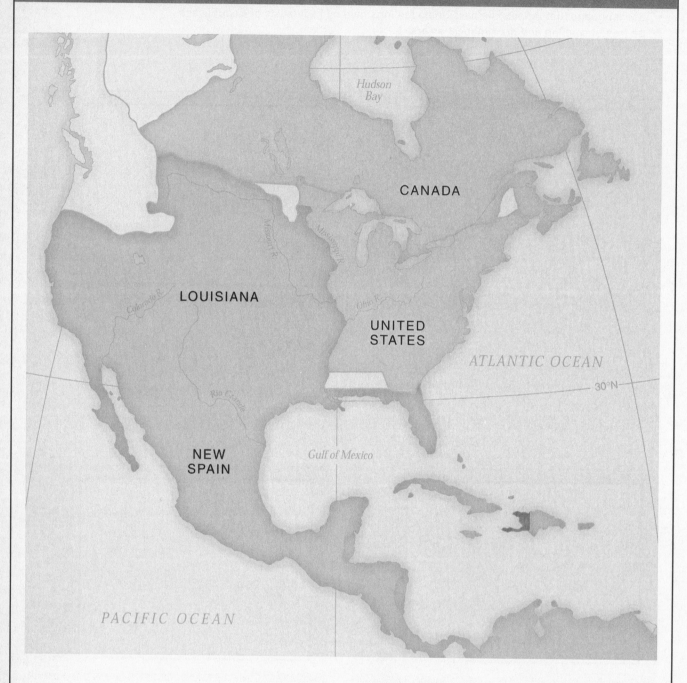

Chapter 12: Foreign Affairs in the Young Nation

PREVIEW 12

Examining Claims in North America in 1796

1. What does this map show?

2. Which countries claimed the most territory in North America in 1796?

3. Which countries claimed the least territory?

4. How did U.S. claims compare with those of other countries?

5. Which peoples' claims are not shown on this map?

6. Who were the United States' potential enemies in 1796?

7. What geographic advantages did the United States have? What geographic disadvantages did it have?

8. If you were president in 1796, what three steps would you take to protect the United States from its more powerful neighbors?
   1.

   2.

   3.

Dilemma 1: What Should President Adams Do to Protect American Ships?

Step 1: Draw a quick sketch of the projected transparency.

Step 2: Read Section 12.3. Annotate the sketch you drew above. Use these words and phrases in your annotations: *envoys, French, attack on ships*.

Step 3: As you watch the mini-play, place Xs on the map below to show where each scene takes place.

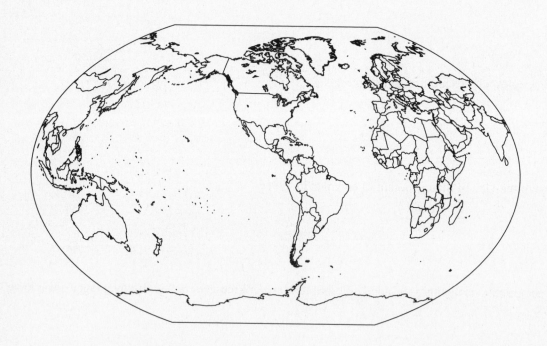

Step 4: Pretend you are citizens living during the presidency of John Adams. Discuss this critical-thinking question with your group: *What should President Adams do to protect American ships?*

    A. Request that Congress declare war on France immediately.
    B. Make a military alliance with Britain and try to beat the French.
    C. Continue to build stronger defenses for American shipping, and negotiate with the French.
    D. Stop American shipping to avoid conflict.

Step 5: Draw an X on the spectrum below to show where your group's choice belongs.

Isolationism ———————————————————— **Involvement**

Step 6: Prepare for a rally at the White House. First, on the sign to the right, write a motto that promotes your group's choice. (Example: "Less Involvement!")

Then write a slogan for your group to chant during the rally. (Example: "No more war!")

Step 7: Write your motto in large, bold letters on a large piece of paper to make a poster. Then quietly practice chanting your slogan.

Step 8: Read Section 12.4 and summarize what actually happened.

Dilemma 2: How Should President Jefferson Deal with Pirates?

Step 1: Draw a quick sketch of the projected transparency.

Step 2: Read Section 12.5. Annotate the sketch you drew above. Use these words and phrases in your annotations: *Barbary pirates, tribute, President Jefferson.*

Step 3: As you watch the mini-play, place Xs on the map below to show where each scene takes place.

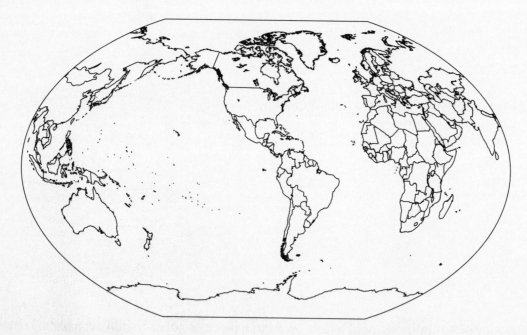

Step 4: Pretend you are citizens living during the presidency of Thomas Jefferson. Discuss this critical-thinking question with your group: *How should President Jefferson deal with pirates?*

A. Pay the increased tribute as requested and avoid bloodshed.
B. Send a peace envoy to negotiate.
C. Send troops to force the pirates to allow American ships to trade freely in the Mediterranean.
D. Order American shipping out of the Mediterranean to avoid unnecessary conflict.

Step 5: Draw an X on the spectrum below to show where your group's choice belongs.

Isolationism   Involvement

Step 6: Prepare for a rally at the White House. First, on the sign to the right, write a motto that promotes your group's choice. (Example: "Less Involvement!")

Then write a slogan for your group to chant during the rally. (Example: "No more war!")

Step 7: Write your motto in large, bold letters on a large piece of paper to make a poster. Then quietly practice chanting your slogan.

Step 8: Read Section 12.6 and summarize what actually happened.

Dilemma 3: What Should President Madison Do to Protect Sailors and Settlers?

Step 1: Draw a quick sketch of the projected transparency.

Step 2: Read Section 12.7. Annotate the sketch you drew above. Use these words and phrases in your annotations: *Britain, impressing, Napoleon*.

Step 3: As you watch the mini-play, place Xs on the map below to show where each scene takes place.

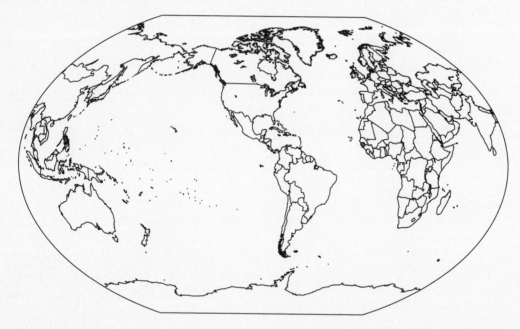

Step 4: Pretend you are citizens living during the presidency of James Madison. Discuss this critical-thinking question with your group: *What should President Madison do to protect sailors and settlers?*

    A. Declare war on Great Britain and attack the British on land and sea.

    B. Declare war on Great Britain, but only wage a war at sea.

    C. Delay declaring war on Great Britain until the country is prepared to win.

    D. Do not declare war on Great Britain. The risks are not worth it.

Step 5: Draw an X on the spectrum below to show where your group's choice belongs.

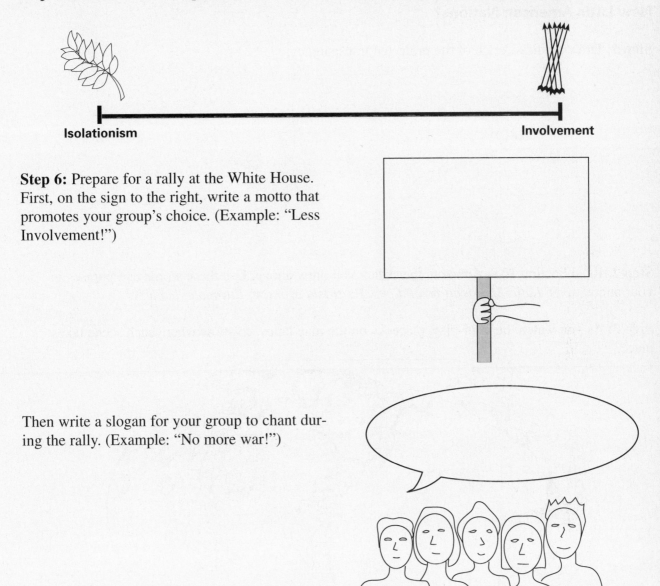

Isolationism — **Involvement**

Step 6: Prepare for a rally at the White House. First, on the sign to the right, write a motto that promotes your group's choice. (Example: "Less Involvement!")

Then write a slogan for your group to chant during the rally. (Example: "No more war!")

Step 7: Write your motto in large, bold letters on a large piece of paper to make a poster. Then quietly practice chanting your slogan.

Step 8: Read Section 12.8 and summarize what actually happened.

Dilemma 4: What Should President Monroe Do to Support the New Latin American Nations?

Step 1: Draw a quick sketch of the projected transparency.

Step 2: Read Section 12.9. Annotate the sketch you drew above. Use these words and phrases in your annotations: *Latin American revolutions, President Monroe, European leaders*.

Step 3: As you watch the mini-play, place Xs on the map below to show where each scene takes place.

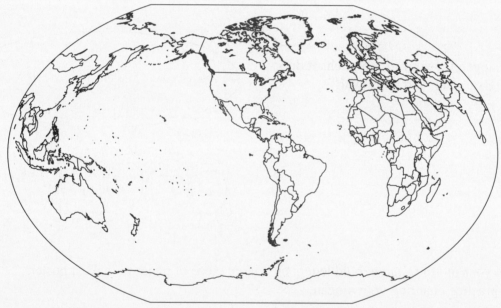

Step 4: Pretend you are citizens living during the presidency of James Monroe. Discuss this critical-thinking question with your group: *What should President Monroe do to support the new Latin American nations?*

    A. Join in an alliance with Great Britain to support Latin American independence.
    B. Do not join an alliance with Great Britain, and warn Europe to stay out of Latin America.
    C. Allow the Latin American countries to defend themselves.
    D. Work to create an alliance with all of the Latin American countries to defend their independence against European interference.

Step 5: Draw an X on the spectrum below to show where your group's choice belongs.

Isolationism

Involvement

Step 6: Prepare for a rally at the White House. First, on the sign to the right, write a motto that promotes your group's choice. (Example: "Less Involvement!")

Then write a slogan for your group to chant during the rally. (Example: "No more war!")

Step 7: Write your motto in large, bold letters on a large piece of paper to make a poster. Then quietly practice chanting your slogan.

Step 8: Read Section 12.10 and summarize what actually happened.

Directions: John Adams was so proud of avoiding war with France that he wanted that fact engraved on his tombstone. On each tombstone below, write a brief inscription to commemorate what the other four presidents accomplished in foreign affairs.

Commemorating Presidential Accomplishments in Foreign Affairs

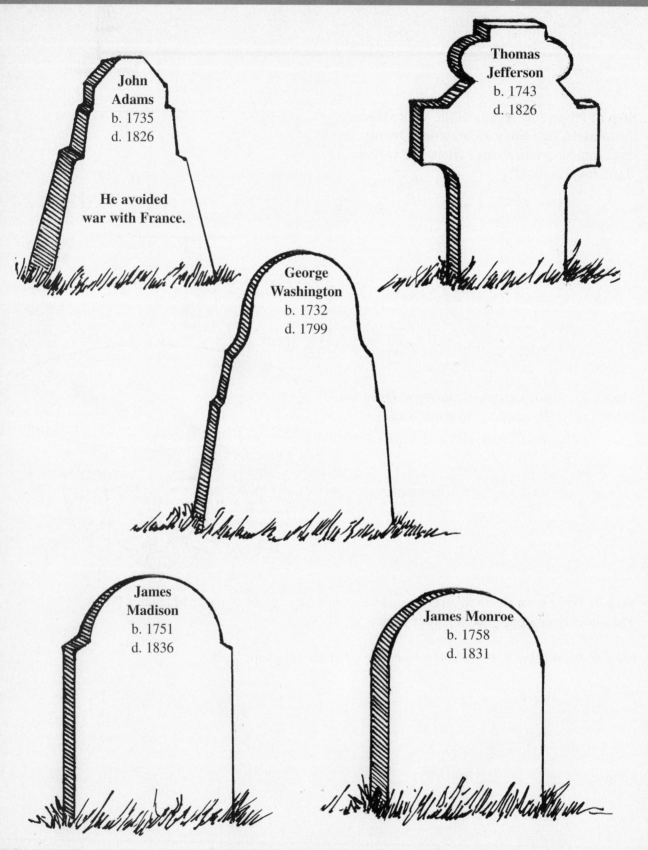

John
Adams
b. 1735
d. 1826

He avoided
war with France.

Thomas
Jefferson
b. 1743
d. 1826

George
Washington
b. 1732
d. 1799

James
Madison
b. 1751
d. 1836

James Monroe
b. 1758
d. 1831

Directions: Write the name of your community in the central hub of the spoke diagram below. Then, for each spoke from the smaller hubs—Geography, Transportation, Economy, and Society—write a word or phrase that describes that aspect of your community. Finally, draw a simple visual for each word or phrase. For example, if you live in Florida, you might write "hot climate" on one of the spokes from the geography hub, and draw a visual of the sun.

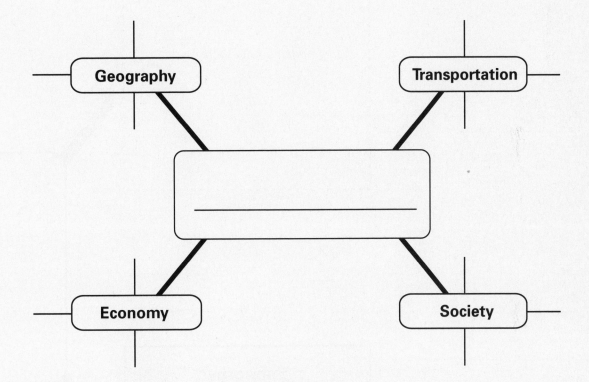

Directions: After you read each section in *History Alive! The United States,* cut out the corresponding drawing from Student Handout 13A and paste it onto the correct hub below. Then, draw at least four spokes from each hub

Geography

paste image here

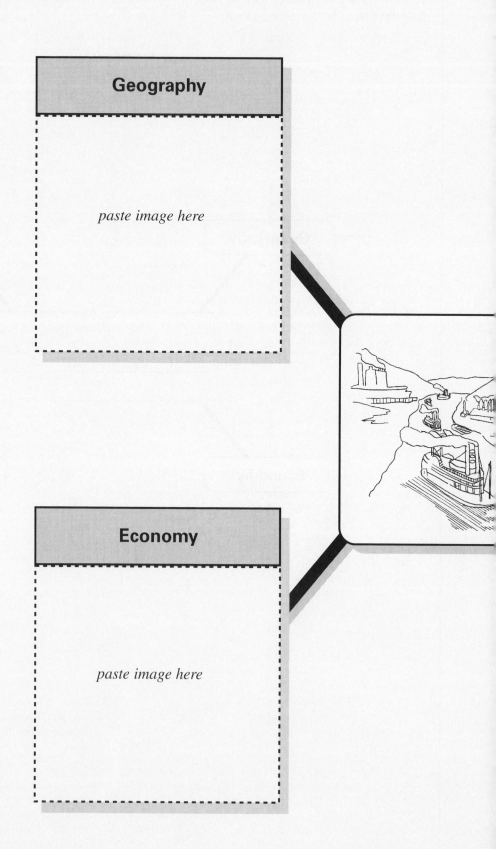

Economy

paste image here

and write a phrase or sentence describing a feature of the topic at the end of each spoke. Draw a simple visual or symbol for each feature.

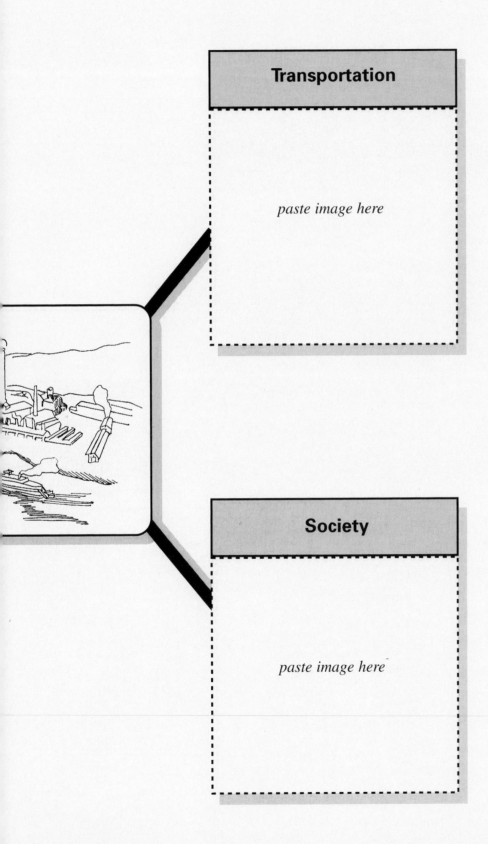

Transportation

paste image here

Society

paste image here

Directions: After you read each section in *History Alive! The United States,* cut out the corresponding drawing from Student Handout 13A and paste it onto the correct hub below. Then, draw at least four spokes from each hub

Geography

paste image here

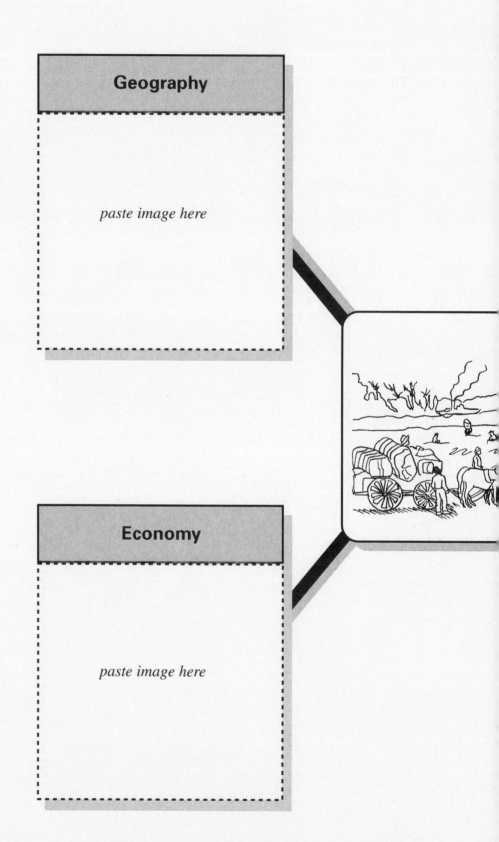

Economy

paste image here

and write a phrase or sentence describing a feature of the topic at the end of each spoke. Draw a simple visual or symbol for each feature.

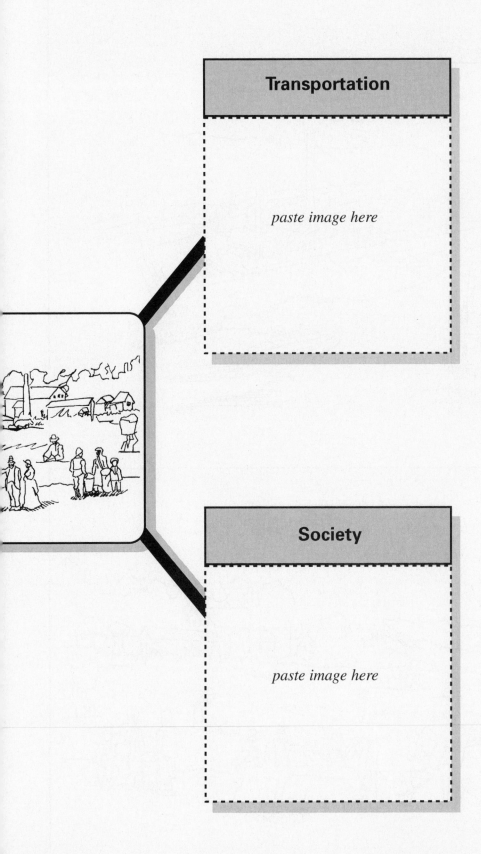

Transportation

paste image here

Society

paste image here

Directions: Label the drawings below "North" or "South." On each drawing, use different colors to highlight key features of geography, economy, transportation, or society of the section. Draw a line from each key feature you highlight and label it (one example has been done for you). Finally, below each drawing, write two statements explaining how geography affected the development of some of the key features you highlighted.

The_____

The_____

Steamboat

Directions: Examine the transparency your teacher projects, and answer the Image Analysis Questions. Share your answers with the class. Then listen to the corresponding song, and answer the Song Analysis Questions. Finally, compare the images and songs. Be prepared to share your answers with the class.

The Federal Period: 1790s

Image Analysis Questions

Based on this painting of President George Washington at a banquet, what were some characteristics of the people who ran the government during the Federal Period? What three words best describe them?

Song Analysis Questions

Listen to the song "The President's March." How does this song make you feel? What are three words that might be used to describe the song? What does the song tell you about our first president?

Directions: Examine the transparency your teacher projects, and answer the Image Analysis Questions. Share your answers with the class. Then listen to the corresponding song, and answer the Song Analysis Questions. Finally, compare the images and songs. Be prepared to share your answers with the class.

The Jacksonian Era: 1820s to 1840s

Image Analysis Questions

Based on this painting of Andrew Jackson meeting the public, what were some characteristics of the people who ran the government during the Jacksonian Era? What three words best describe Jackson and his supporters?

Song Analysis Questions

Listen to the song "The Hunters of Kentucky." The song was written for Andrew Jackson's 1828 presidential campaign. How does the song make you feel? What are three words that might be used to describe the song? What does the song tell you about our sixth president?

Contrasting Images and Songs

Based on the images and songs you have analyzed, how do you think the Jacksonian Era was different from the Federal Period? What do you think accounts for the differences?

READING NOTES 14

Directions: After you read each section in your text, record notes as directed.

14.2 The Inauguration of Andrew Jackson

Write a paragraph summary of this section that includes these terms: *democracy, common man, vote, rich and well-born*.

Add facial expressions and speech bubbles to the drawing below to reflect what the common man and the rich and well-born felt and thought about Jackson's rise from the frontier to the White House.

Directions: After you read each section in your text, record notes as directed.

14.3 From the Frontier to the White House

Write a paragraph summary of this section that includes these terms: *Battle of New Orleans, Democratic Party, corrupt bargain, self-made man.*

Add facial expressions and speech bubbles to the drawing below to reflect what the common man and the rich and well-born felt and thought about Jackson's rise from the frontier to the White House.

Directions: After you read each section in your text, record notes as directed.

14.4 Jackson's Approach to Governing

Write a paragraph summary of this section that includes these terms: *kitchen cabinet, spoils system, civil servant.*

Add facial expressions and speech bubbles to the drawing below to reflect how the common man and the rich and well-born felt and thought about Jackson's approach to governing.

Directions: After you read each section in your text, record notes as directed.

14.5 The Nullification Crisis

Write a paragraph summary of this section that includes these terms: *tariffs, states' rights, South Carolina, John C. Calhoun.*

Add a facial expression and a speech bubble to the drawing below to reflect what a states' rights believer thought about the nullification crisis.

Directions: After you read each section in your text, record notes as directed.

14.6 Jackson Battles the Bank of the United States

Write a paragraph summary that includes these terms: *Nicholas Biddle, Henry Clay, farmers, Bank of the United States*.

Add facial expressions and speech bubbles to the drawing below to reflect how the common people and the rich and well-born felt and thought about Jackson's battle with the Bank of the United States.

Directions: After you read each section in your text, record notes as directed.

14.7 Jackson's Indian Policy

Write a paragraph summary of this section that includes these terms: *Cherokees, Black Hawk, Trail of Tears.*

Add facial expressions and speech bubbles to the drawing below to reflect how Native Americans and the common man felt and thought about Jackson's Indian policy.

Directions: Use the information you learned in this activity to evaluate Andrew Jackson's impact on American society. Create a hero's commemorative plaque for Jackson that emphasizes his positive contributions to American democracy, and a "Wanted" poster that shows his negative impact on American democracy. Make sure you include

- two sketches of Andrew Jackson.
- two sentences stating why Jackson should be praised (below the commemorative plaque).
- two sentences stating why Jackson should be condemned (below the "Wanted" poster).
- a one-paragraph answer to the following question: In your opinion, was Andrew Jackson more of a villain or a hero?

Andrew Jackson
A National Hero

WANTED
Andrew Jackson

_____   _____

_____   _____

_____   _____

_____   _____

_____   _____

_____   _____

_____   _____

_____

_____

_____

_____

Directions: Imagine that you can go back in time and change any historical event. What event would you change? How would you make it different, and why? Write your answer below.

Changing History

Directions: Read Section 15.2 in *History Alive! The United States* up to the subhead "A Noble Bargain."

Situation 1: Louisiana Purchase

What action should the United States take? Circle your choice.

A. Offer to buy the city of New Orleans from France so that American farmers can export their goods from that port.

B. Threaten to go to war if France does not hand over New Orleans to the United States.

C. Offer to buy all of the Louisiana Territory, including New Orleans, so that the French are no longer a threat to the United States.

Explain your choice: The United States should select option _____ because…

Read the remainder of Section 15.2 to find out what happened. Then, on the map below, draw the boundaries of the newly acquired territory and annotate the map. Use these three terms in your annotations: *Thomas Jefferson, Louisiana Territory, France.*

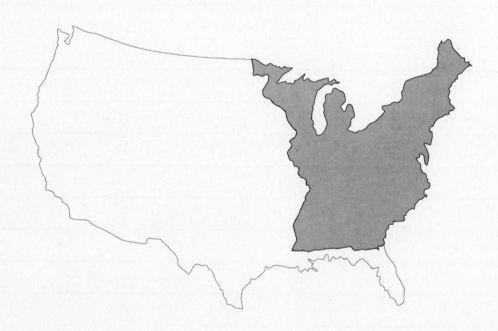

Directions: Read Section 15.3 in *History Alive! The United States* up to the subhead "Govern or Get Out."

Situation 2: Florida

What action should the United States take? Circle your choice.

A. Use military force to take Florida from Spain since Andrew Jackson's invasion proves that Spain's army is weak.

B. Apologize to Spain for Jackson's invasion. Send troops to patrol the border between Florida and the United States to prevent raids by Indians and runaway slaves.

C. Offer to buy Florida in order to avoid war with Spain.

Explain your choice: The United States should select option _____ because...

Read the remainder of Section 15.3 to find out what happened. Then, on the map below, draw the boundaries of the newly acquired territory and annotate the map. Use these three terms in your annotations: *Spain, Andrew Jackson, runaway slaves.*

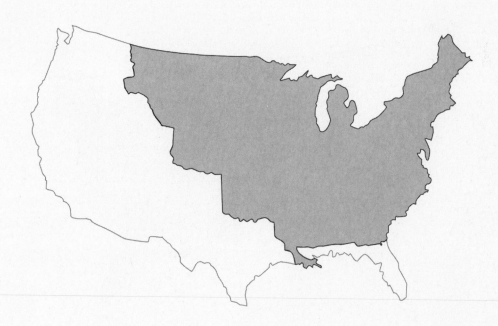

Directions: Read Section 15.4 in *History Alive! The United States* up to the subhead "To Annex Texas or Not?"

Situation 3: Texas

What action should the United States take? Circle your choice.

A. Let Texas remain an independent country. Try to establish good relations with Texas, and avoid angering Mexico.

B. Annex Texas to the United States and risk war with Mexico.

C. Make a treaty with Mexico agreeing to split Texas between the two countries.

Explain your choice: The United States should select option _____ because…

Read the remainder of Section 15.4 to find out what happened. Then, on the map below, draw the boundaries of the newly acquired territory and annotate the map. Use these three terms in your annotations: *Stephen Austin, Mexico, Alamo*.

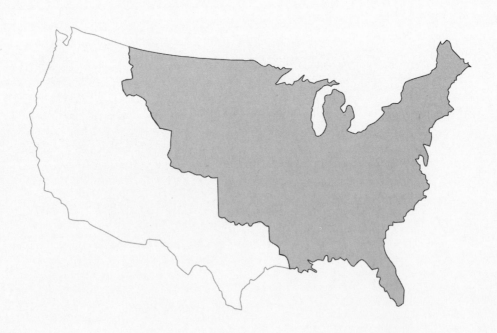

Directions: Read Section 15.5 in *History Alive! The United States* up to the subhead "All of Oregon or Half?"

Situation 4: Oregon Country

What action should the United States take? Circle your choice.

A.   Annex all of Oregon to the United States and risk war with Britain.

B.   Offer to sell Oregon to Britain in order to increase the money in the United States Treasury.

C.   Make a treaty with Britain agreeing to divide Oregon between the two countries.

Explain your choice: The United States should select option _____ because…

Read the remainder of Section 15.5 to find out what happened. Then, on the map below, draw the boundaries of the newly acquired territory and annotate the map. Use these three terms in your annotations: *Britain, 49th parallel, pioneers.*

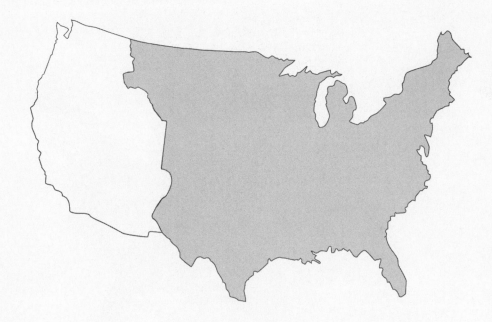

Directions: Read Section 15.6 in *History Alive! The United States* up to the subhead "The Treaty of Guadalupe Hidalgo."

Situation 5: War with Mexico

What action should the United States take?

A. Apologize for invading Mexico, offer to buy California and New Mexico, and accept the Nueces River as the border between Texas and Mexico.

B. Demand that Mexico recognize the Rio Grande as the border of Texas and cede (give up) California and New Mexico to the United States.

C. Annex all of Mexico to the United States because it is weak after losing the Mexican War.

Explain your choice: The United States should select option _____ because…

Read the remainder of Section 15.6 to find out what happened. Then, on the map below, draw the boundaries of the newly acquired territory and annotate the map. Use these three terms in your annotations: *Treaty of Guadalupe Hidalgo, Rio Grande, California.*

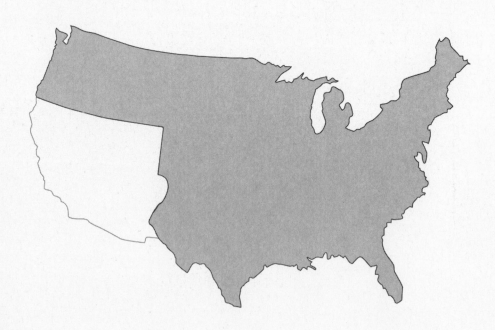

PROCESSING 15

Directions: Select six characters from the drawing below (you may include animals), and create speech or thought bubbles for each one. In each bubble, write one or two sentences describing the character's thoughts or feelings. Within each bubble, use one of the terms listed in the Word Bank. If necessary, write your sentences as captions in the space below the drawing. Color in the drawing to make it look like the actual painting.

Annotating a Famous Historical Painting

Word Bank

destroy	Manifest Destiny	progress
growth	native people	territorial acquisition
justified	other countries	United States

Directions: Listen to the song "Sweet Betsy from Pike" and read along with the lyrics on the opposite page. After listening, answer these questions.

Analyzing the Folk Song "Sweet Betsy from Pike"

1. What is the mood of the song's melody?

2. Where was Sweet Betsy headed?

3. Why would Sweet Betsy, and pioneers like those in the image, be willing to risk such hardships?

4. This folk song was written in the 1800s, as many people were moving to the West. Why would a song like this have been written?

5. Why do you think this survived to be a folk song today?

Sweet Betsy from Pike

Oh, do you remember Sweet Betsy from Pike
Who crossed the wide prairie with her lover Ike?
With two yoke of oxen, a big yellow dog,
A tall Shanghai rooster, and one spotted hog.
CHORUS:

Sing too rali oorali oorali ay
Sing too rali oorali oorali ay

One evening quite early they camped on the Platte,
'Twas near by the road on a green shady flat;
Where Betsy, quite tired, lay down to repose,
While with wonder Ike gazed on his Pike County rose.
CHORUS

The warriors came down in a wild yelling horde,
And Betsy was skeered they would scalp her adored;
Behind the front wagon wheel Betsy did crawl,
And fought off the warriors with musket and ball.
CHORUS

They soon reached the desert, where Betsy gave out,
And down in the sand she lay rolling about;
While Ike in great terror looked on in surprise,
Saying, "Get up now, Betsy, you'll get sand in your eyes."
CHORUS

They stopped at Salt Lake to inquire the way,
And Brigham invited Ike and Betsy to stay.
But Betsy declined, said the weather's too hot
It's too isolated in this desert spot.
CHORUS

The alkali desert was burning and bare,
And Isaac's soul shrank from the death that lurked there:
"Dear old Pike County, I'll go back to you."
Says Betsy, "You'll go by yourself if you do."
CHORUS

The wagon tipped over with a terrible crash,
And out on the prairie rolled all sorts of trash;
A few little baby clothes done up with care
Sweet Betsy was worried they might have a tear.
CHORUS

The Shanghai ran off and the cattle all died,
The last piece of bacon that morning was fried;
Poor Ike got discouraged, and Betsy got mad,
The dog wagged his tail and looked wonderfully sad.
CHORUS

They swam the wide rivers and crossed the tall peaks,
And camped on the prairie for weeks upon weeks.
Starvation and cholera and hard work and slaughter,
They reached California spite of hell and high water.
CHORUS x2

READING NOTES 16

Directions: Before each minidrama, read the corresponding section in *History Alive! The United States.* Then fill in the box for that group.

16.2 The Explorers

Reasons they moved to the West:

Hardships they faced:

Legacies they left:

16.4 The Californios

Reasons they moved to the West:

Hardships they faced:

Legacies they left:

16.3 The Mountain Men

Reasons they moved to the West:

Hardships they faced:

Legacies they left:

16.5 The Missionaries

Reasons they moved to the West:

Hardships they faced:

Legacies they left:

Directions: Before each minidrama, read the corresponding section in *History Alive! The United States.* Then fill in the box for that group.

16.6 The Pioneer Women

Reasons they moved to the West:

Hardships they faced:

Legacies they left:

16.8 The Forty-Niners

Reasons they moved to the West:

Hardships they faced:

Legacies they left:

16.7 The Mormons

Reasons they moved to the West:

Hardships they faced:

Legacies they left:

16.9 The Chinese

Reasons they moved to the West:

Hardships they faced:

Legacies they left:

Directions: Create a folk song that details the experiences of the people who moved to the West. Each student should write the lyrics for his or her own folk song.

Songs of the West

1. Choose a tune you know well to provide the melody. You may use the tune of "Sweet Betsy from Pike" or any other folk song, such as "Clementine" or "I've Been Working on the Railroad."
2. Write at least four, four-line stanzas.
3. Include four different groups from the West in your song. Each stanza should be about a different group. Within the four lines of each stanza, include
   - reasons this group moved to the West.
   - hardships this group endured.
   - legacies this group left to the West.

Directions: Use what you have learned about mule packing to write a dialogue between the Mexicano and Anglo characters in the drawing. The dialogue should accurately reflect what a Mexicano and an Anglo settler might have said to each other. Include each of the following terms at least once in the dialogue: *mule packing, important, help, geography, contribution, gracias* (thank you).

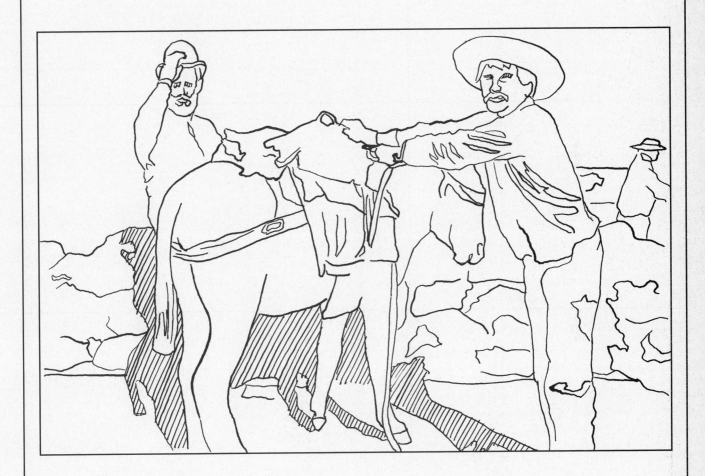

Directions: After you analyze the image at a station, find the section in your book that corresponds to the image. Write the section title and corresponding placard letter in the appropriate boxes. Then read the section, and write

Section Number and Title	Placard Letter	Examples of Mexicano Contributions
17.2		
17.3		
17.4		
17.5		

specific examples of the Mexicano contributions and why they were used by Anglo settlers. Finally, create a simple drawing or symbol to represent the contributions.

Why Contributions Were Used	Visual of Contributions

Directions: After you analyze the image at a station, find the section in your book that corresponds to the image. Write the section title and corresponding placard letter in the appropriate boxes. Then read the section, and write

Section Number and Title	Placard Letter	Examples of Mexicano Contributions
17.6		
17.7		
17.8		
17.9		
17.10		

specific examples of the Mexicano contributions and why they were used by Anglo settlers. Finally, create a simple drawing or symbol to represent the contributions.

Why Contributions Were Used	Visual of Contributions

Directions: Show Mexicano contributions to the Southwest by annotating the map below. Follow these steps:
1) Create or find a visual symbol to represent each of the Mexicano contributions to the Southwest. 2) Place your symbol near the geographic region(s) where the contribution was used.

The introduction of a better breed of sheep increased wool production in the U.S. more than 300%

3) Annotate the map with one sentence identifying the contribution and describing its importance. One example has been done for you.

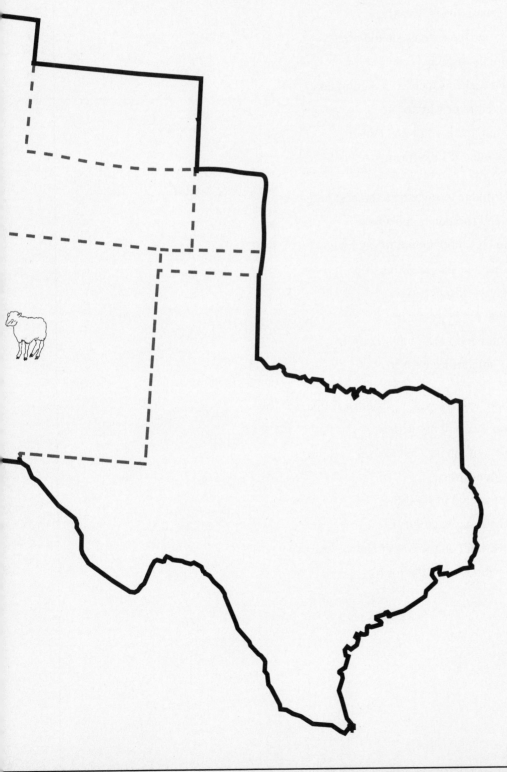

Directions: Listen to the song "Let Us All Speak Our Minds." Follow along with the lyrics below. Afterward, answer the questions on the next page.

Analyzing "Let Us All Speak Our Minds"

Men tell us 'tis fit that wives should submit

To their husbands submissively, weakly;

Tho' whatever they say, their wives should obey

Unquestioning, stupidly, meekly.

Our husbands would make us their own dictum take

Without ever a wherefore or why for it.

But I don't and I can't and I won't and I shan't,

No, I will speak my mind if I die for it.

For we know it's all fudge to say man's the best judge

Of what should be and shouldn't, and so on.

That woman should bow, nor attempt to say how

She considers that matters should go on.

I never yet gave up myself thus a slave,

However my husband might try for it;

For I can't and I won't and I shan't and I don't,

But I will speak my mind if I die for it.

And all ladies, I hope, who've with husbands to cope,

With the rights of the sex will not trifle.

We all, if we choose, our tongues but to use,

Can all opposition soon stifle;

Let man, if he will, then bid us be still

And silent, a price he'll pay high for it.

For we won't and we can't and we don't and we shan't,

Let us all speak our minds if we die for it.

LUCRETIA MOTT. JULIA WARD HOWE. SUSAN B. ANTHONY. DOROTHEA LYNDE DIX.

1. What is the mood of the song's melody? What emotions are expressed in the lyrics? Do the melody and lyrics seem to go together? Why or why not?

2. Why do you think women like those pictured above would write and sing a song like this?

3. Do you think this song's message still has meaning today? Why or why not?

Directions: Read Sections 18.2 through 18.7. Follow these steps to take notes on each section: 1) Find the figure below whose sign's symbol best matches the information you read. 2) Create an appropriate slogan for the reform movement associated with that figure. 3) Write the slogan next to the symbol on the sign.

Sprouting Seeds of Reform!

Why did the Second Great Awakening encourage reform? People were encouraged to save their souls through good works.

Goal of the movement:

Conditions before the movement:

Grievances:

Why did the election of Andrew Jackson encourage reform? *He showed that a single individual could change society.*

Leaders of the movement:

Leaders of the movement:

4) Write the name of the reform movement or event near the figure. 5) Write notes about the reform movement in the appropriate sections. (The first figure is partially completed for you.)

Conditions before reform:

Conditions before reform:

Advances achieved:

Reform leader:

Reforms:

Reform leader:

Reforms:

ACTIVITY NOTES 18

Critical-Thinking Prompts for Women's Issues

Excerpt A

"He has never permitted her to exercise her inalienable [undeniable] right to the elective franchise [vote]. He has compelled her to submit to laws, in the formation of which she had no voice."

1. Rewrite the above excerpt from the Declaration of Sentiments, using simpler language that a classmate would understand.

2. Discuss in your group the degree to which this grievance has been redressed today. Place an X on the spectrum below to represent your group's decision.

|————————————————————|————————————————————|

Not Redressed at All   Somewhat Redressed   Totally Redressed

3. List facts and information your group used to come to your decision.

Critical-Thinking Prompts for Women's Issues

Excerpt B

"He has monopolized [dominated] nearly all the profitable employments, and from those she is permitted to follow, she receives but a scanty remuneration [pay]."

1. Rewrite the above excerpt from the Declaration of Sentiments, using simpler language a classmate would understand.

2. Discuss in your group the degree to which this grievance has been redressed today. Place an X on the spectrum below to represent your group's decision.

|————————————————————|————————————————————|

Not Redressed at All   Somewhat Redressed   Totally Redressed

3. List facts and information your group used to come to your decision.

ACTIVITY NOTES 18

Excerpt C

"He has denied her the facilities for obtaining a thorough education, all colleges being closed against her."

1. Rewrite the above excerpt from the Declaration of Sentiments, using simpler language a classmate would understand.

2. Discuss in your group the degree to which this grievance has been redressed today. Place an X on the spectrum below to represent your group's decision.

Not Redressed at All   Somewhat Redressed   Totally Redressed

3. List facts and information your group used to come to your decision.

Critical-Thinking Prompts for Women's Issues

Excerpt D

"He has created a false sense of public sentiment by giving to the world a different code of morals for men and women."

1. Rewrite the above excerpt from the Declaration of Sentiments, using simpler language a classmate would understand.

2. Discuss in your group the degree to which this grievance has been redressed today. Place an X on the spectrum
   below to represent your group's decision.

Not Redressed at All   Somewhat Redressed   Totally Redressed

3. List facts and information your group used to come to your decision.

Directions: Write a letter to Elizabeth Cady Stanton that updates her on how much progress women have made in America today. Your letter should include the following:

Letter to a Woman Reformer

- date and proper salutation (i.e., "Dear Ms. Stanton…")
- an update on the degree to which two grievances outlined in the Declaration of Sentiments have been redressed today
- at least three facts or pieces of information to support each of your updates
- a conclusion summarizing your opinion regarding where women have made the greatest progress and where work still needs to be done
- a memento from the Seneca Falls Convention, such as a program, button, or poster. Make sure the memento includes the date and location of the convention, names of the key organizers, and the main reason for the convention

Directions: First, examine the transparency your teacher projects, and answer the Image Analysis Questions. Share your answers with the class. Then, listen to the song "Moses" when your teacher plays it, and read the lyrics on the transparency. Write responses to the Song Analysis Questions.

Image Analysis Questions

1. What object do you see?

2. What images and symbols does it contain?

3. What story do you think it shows?

4. How do you think the image relates to the Bible and to the experience of slavery?

Song Analysis Questions

1. What is the tone of the song?

2. What Bible story is told in the song?

3. How does the song relate to the images in the quilt square?

4. How might the song and the quilt square relate to the experience of slavery?

Directions: Read the quotation your teacher has given to you. Then, circulate around the room to locate the placard that best matches the quotation. Once you have located the placard, find the matching section of your Reading Notes and complete the steps.

Placard 19A

1. Match the placard with the quotation.

Placard 19A: Working Conditions of Slaves matches Quotation _____

2. Analyze the placard. Imagine you are one of the slaves pictured here. Describe how three of the following parts of your body feel: fingers, back, legs, head, eyes, arms.

3. Find and read the matching section in *History Alive! The United States*. Record four key ideas about this topic.

4. Sketch four symbols and/or illustrations for a quilt square on this topic.

Placard 19B

1. Match the placard with the quotation.

Placard 19B: Living Conditions of Slaves matches Quotation _____

2. Analyze the placard. Imagine you are a visitor to this scene. How might these slaves feel about their situation?

3. Find and read the matching section in *History Alive! The United States*. Record four key ideas about this topic.

4. Sketch four symbols and/or illustrations for a quilt square on this topic.

Placard 19C

1. Match the placard with the quotation.

Placard 19C: Controlling Slaves matches Quotation _____

2. Analyze the placard. How could the scene pictured have happened?

3. Find and read the matching section in *History Alive! The United States*. Record four methods that slave owners used to control slaves.

4. Sketch four symbols and/or illustrations for a quilt square on this topic.

Placard 19D

1. Match the placard with the quotation.

Placard 19D: Resistance to Slavery matches Quotation _____

2. Analyze the placard. What is happening in the image?

3. Find and read the matching section in *History Alive! The United States*. Record at least five ways that slaves stood up to their masters.

4. Sketch four symbols and/or illustrations for a quilt square on this topic.

Directions: Read the quotation your teacher has given to you. Then, circulate around the room to locate the placard that best matches the quotation. Once you have located the placard, find the matching section of your Reading Notes and complete the steps.

Placard 19E

1. Match the placard with the quotation.

Placard 19E: Slave Families and Communities matches Quotation _____

2. Analyze the placard. Describe how three of the people in this scene might feel about what is happening.

3. Find and read the matching section in *History Alive! The United States*. Record two positive and two negative aspects of slave families and communities.

4. Sketch four symbols and/or illustrations for a quilt square on this topic.

Placard 19F

1. Match the placard with the quotation.

Placard 19F: Leisure Time Activities matches Quotation _____

2. Analyze the placard. Describe what three different people are doing.

3. Find and read the matching section in *History Alive! The United States*. List at least four ways slaves spent their leisure time.

4. Sketch four symbols and/or illustrations for a quilt square on this topic.

Placard 19G

1. Match the placard with the quotation.

Placard 19G: Slave Churches matches
Quotation _____

2. Analyze the placard. Imagine you are a visitor to
this scene. Describe what you see and hear.

3. Find and read the matching section in *History
Alive! The United States*. Explain why the idea of
being invisible was important to slave churches.

4. Sketch four symbols and/or illustrations
for a quilt square on this topic.

Placard 19H

1. Match the placard with the quotation.

Placard 19H: African American Culture matches
Quotation _____

2. Analyze the placard. Imagine you are a visitor to
this scene. Describe what you hear, including a direct
quotation from one of the slaves shown in the image.

3. Find and read the matching section in *History
Alive! The United States*. Record four aspects of
African American life that have their roots in African culture.

4. Sketch four symbols and/or illustrations
for a quilt square on this topic.

PREVIEW 20

Directions: Imagine that you have an older brother with whom you must share a television set. Your brother loves to watch professional wrestling, but you hate it. Furthermore, wrestling is on at the same time as your favorite show. Which of the following options do you believe is the best solution to your problem? Explain your choice.

a. Give in to your brother and let him watch the wrestling because he is older and should have more privileges.

b. Challenge him to a fight, and whoever wins has the right to watch what he or she wants.

c. Ask your brother to meet with you and discuss ways you can share the television equally.

Directions: Listen to the CD your teacher plays, and follow along in *History Alive! The United States.* Complete the information in Part 1. Discuss the issue with your group. After your group

20.2 Confronting the Issue of Slavery

When Missouri applied for statehood, Congress had to confront the problem of the spread of slavery into the territories.

Part 1

Issue 1: Missouri applied for statehood as a slave state.	
Northerners favored/opposed (circle one) this because	Southerners favored/opposed (circle one) this because

Issue 2: The Tallmadge Amendment proposed that Missouri be admitted as a free state.	
Northerners favored/opposed (circle one) this because	Southerners favored/opposed (circle one) this because

Part 2

Given these two issues, create a compromise that satisfies northerners and southerners.

Part 3

Read Section 20.3. What actually happened?

reaches a compromise, complete Part 2. Read what actually happened in *History Alive! The United States,* and record notes in Part 3.

20.4 The Missouri Compromise Unravels
The issue of slavery continued to divide the nation.

Part 1

Issue 1: Abolitionists wanted to stop slavery in Washington, D.C., but Congress refused to consider anti-slavery petitions.	
Northern abolitionists were pleased/angered (circle one) because	Southerners were pleased/angered (circle one) because

Issue 2: Some northerners assisted fugitive slaves.	
Northerners tolerated/condemned (circle one) this practice because	Southerners tolerated/condemned (circle one) this practice because

Issue 3: The Wilmot Proviso stated slavery would not be allowed in the Mexican Cession.	
Northerners favored/opposed (circle one) this amendment because	Southerners favored/opposed (circle one) this amendment because

Issue 4: California applied for admission as a free state.	
Northerners favored/opposed (circle one) admitting California as a free state because	Southerners favored/opposed (circle one) admitting California as a free state because

Part 2

Given these four issues, create a compromise that satisfies northerners and southerners.

Part 3

Read Section 20.5. What actually happened?

Directions: Listen to the CD your teacher plays, and follow along in *History Alive! The United States.* Complete the information in Part 1. Discuss the issue with your group. After your group

20.6 The Compromise Satisfies No One

In spite of the Compromise of 1850, the dispute over slavery became increasingly bitter.

Part 1

Issue 1: The Fugitive Slave Law caused bitterness between the North and the South.	
Northerners were satisfied/dissatisfied (circle one) with the way the Fugitive Slave Law was enforced because	Southerners were satisfied/dissatisfied (circle one) with the way the Fugitive Slave Law was enforced because

Issue 2: The book *Uncle Tom's Cabin* told the story of a slave and his master.	
The book was popular/unpopular (circle one) in the North because	The books was popular/unpopular (circle one) in the South because

Issue 3: The Kansas-Nebraska Act stated that the issue of slavery in those territories would be decided by popular sovereignty. Both pro-slavery and anti-slavery forces rushed to the territories to vote.	
Northerners were pleased/unhappy (circle one) about the act because	Southerners were pleased/unhappy (circle one) about the act because

Issue 4: The *Dred Scott* case. Scott was a slave who believed his trip to Wisconsin made him a free man.	
Northerners probably believed he was free/still a slave (circle one) because	Southerners probably believed he was free/still a slave (circle one) because

Part 2

Recommend a ruling to the Supreme Court on the *Dred Scott* case that satisfies northerners and southerners. Your ruling must address these issues: Was Scott a citizen with the right to sue in federal court? Did Scott's visit to Wisconsin make him a free man? Can Congress ban slavery in the territories?

Part 3

Read Section 20.7. What actually happened?

reaches a compromise, complete Part 2. Read what actually happened in *History Alive! The United States,* and record notes in Part 3.

20.8 From Compromise to Crisis

In the late 1850s, compromise between pro-slavery and anti-slavery forces became almost impossible.

Part 1

Issue 1: During the Lincoln-Douglas debates, positions regarding slavery were made clear.	
Lincoln, representing the opinion of the North, felt slavery was a legal/moral (circle one) issue because	Douglas, representing the opinion of the South, felt slavery was a legal/moral (circle one) issue because

Issue 2: John Brown attacked the arsenal at Harpers Ferry to get weapons for a slave rebellion.	
Some northerners upset/reassured (circle one) southerners after Brown's raid because	Southerners were unconcerned/fearful (circle one) about Brown's raid because

Issue 3: In 1860 Abraham Lincoln was elected president.	
Northerners were happy/unhappy (circle one) about the election because	Southerners were happy/unhappy (circle one) with the election because

Part 2

Given these three issues, create a compromise that satisfies northerners and southerners and can save the Union.

Part 3

Read Section 20.9. What actually happened?

PROCESSING 20

Directions: Write a letter from the perspective that you took in the activity (either northern or southern) in which you accuse the other side of causing the Civil War. Your letter should
- include a description of your position on slavery.
- include an explanation of why you feel the other side caused compromises to fail.
- be five to six sentences long.

Who Is Responsible for the Civil War?

Directions: After you have finished your letter, exchange notebooks with a student who has written from the opposing perspective. For example, if you wrote a northerner's letter, exchange your letter with a southerner. On the page opposite their letter, write a rebuttal to what he or she has written, and then reexchange notebooks.

Response to My Opponent's Letter

Directions: As you listen to each song, answer the questions below.

Civil War Songs: Changing Attitudes toward War

"The Bonnie Blue Flag"

What three words best describe the mood of this song?

If you were a Civil War soldier from the South, like the one shown here, how would this song make you feel?

"Tenting Tonight"

What three words best describe the mood of this song?

What do you think a Civil War soldier from the North, like the one shown here, would say to the person who wrote the first song?

Directions: Read Sections 21.3 through 21.8 in *History Alive! The United States.* Answer the questions for each section.

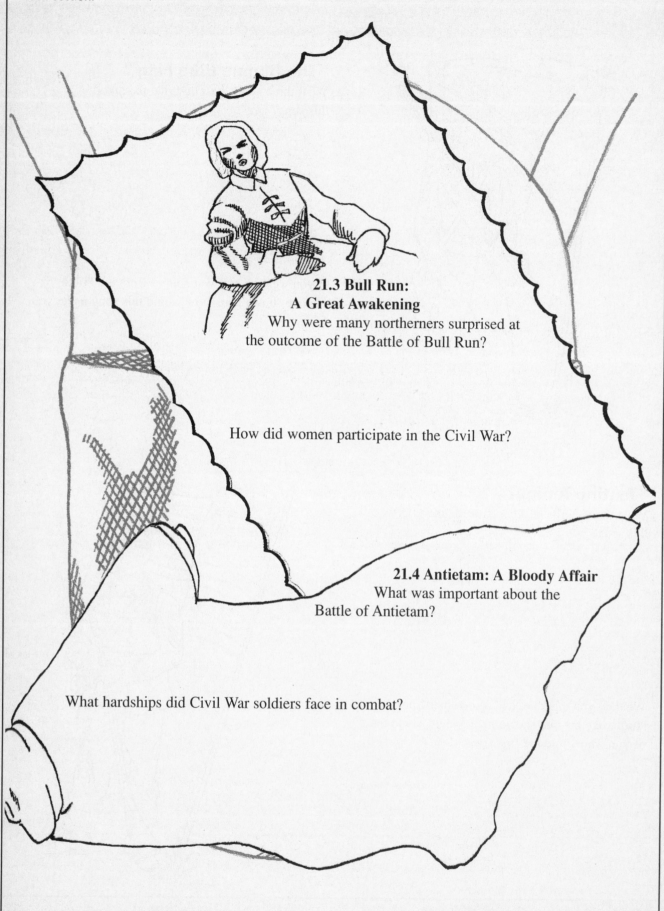

21.3 Bull Run: A Great Awakening

Why were many northerners surprised at the outcome of the Battle of Bull Run?

How did women participate in the Civil War?

21.4 Antietam: A Bloody Affair

What was important about the Battle of Antietam?

What hardships did Civil War soldiers face in combat?

RALLY ROUND

THE FLAG BOYS!

100 MEN WANTED!!

21.5 Gettysburg: A Turning Point
Why was the Battle of Gettysburg considered a turning point in the Civil War?

What problems developed on the Union home front during the war?

21.6 Vicksburg: A Besieged City
Why was the Union victory at Vicksburg important?

What problems developed on the Confederate home front during the war?

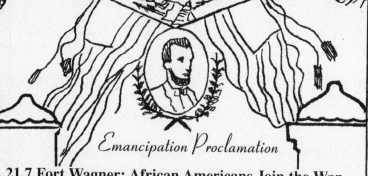

Emancipation Proclamation

21.7 Fort Wagner: African Americans Join the War
What was important about the actions of the Massachusetts 54th at Fort Wagner?

How did African Americans contribute to the Union war effort?

21.8 Appomattox: Total War Brings an End

What is meant by "total war"? What did the Union army do during their campaign of total war?

What terms did Grant offer Lee when he surrendered at Appomattox Courthouse?

Directions: Draw heads and facial features to express how three individuals felt about the end of the Civil War. Include the following: a Union or a Confederate soldier, a northern or a southern citizen, and an African American. Make thought bubbles above the heads showing what each individual might be thinking. Each thought bubble should

- describe how fighting in the Civil War affected the individual's life.
- explain how the end of the Civil War might change the individual's life.
- be free of misspellings and grammatical errors.

PREVIEW 22

Gaining and Losing Student Rights: Like the Gains and Losses of African American Citizenship Rights During Reconstruction

Classroom Experience	Historical Event

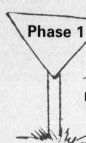

Phase 1

22.2 Presidential Reconstruction

Directions: Read Section 22.2 in *History Alive! The United States,* and follow the steps below.

Event Bank:
Thirteenth Amendment
Johnson's Reconstruction
Freedmen's Bureau
black codes

FULL CITIZENSHIP

1. Write a short description of each event in the Event Bank that helped African Americans achieve full citizenship.

2. Write a short description of each event in the Event Bank that kept African Americans from achieving full citizenship.

LIMITED CITIZENSHIP

3. Review the items in the Event Bank. Next to each event, write plusses (+) or minuses (−) to show how many steps toward or away from full citizenship African Americans took during this event.

one + or −: minor step forward or back

two + + or − − : medium step forward or back

three + + + or − − − : major step forward or back

4. When directed, draw an X on the spectrum below to show where African Americans were at the end of this phase.

Limited Citizenship   **Full Citizenship**

Phase 2

22.3 Congressional Reconstruction

Directions: Read Section 22.3 in *History Alive! The United States,* and follow the steps below.

Event Bank:
Civil Rights Act of 1866
Fourteenth Amendment
Military Reconstruction Act
Johnson's impeachment
sharecropping

 FULL CITIZENSHIP

1. Write a short description of each event in the Event Bank that helped African Americans achieve full citizenship.

2. Write a short description of each event in the Event Bank that kept African Americans from achieving full citizenship.

LIMITED CITIZENSHIP

3. Review the items in the Event Bank. Next to each event, write plusses (+) or minuses (−) to show how many steps toward or away from full citizenship African Americans took during this event.

one + or − : minor step forward or back
two + + or − − : medium step forward or back
three + + + or − − − : major step forward or back

4. When directed, draw an X on the spectrum below to show where African Americans were at the end of this phase.

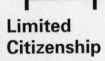

Limited Citizenship

Full Citizenship

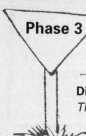

Phase 3

22.4 Southern Reconstruction

Directions: Read Section 22.4 in *History Alive! The United States,* and follow the steps below.

Event Bank:
Fifteenth Amendment
new state constitutions
African American office-holders

FULL CITIZENSHIP

1. Write a short description of each event in the Event Bank that helped African Americans achieve full citizenship.

2. Write a short description of each event in the Event Bank that kept African Americans from achieving full citizenship.

LIMITED CITIZENSHIP

3. Review the items in the Event Bank. Next to each event, write plusses (+) or minuses (−) to show how many steps toward or away from full citizenship African Americans took during this event.

one + or − : minor step forward or back
two + + or − − : medium step forward or back
three + + + or − − − : major step forward or back

4. When directed, draw an X on the spectrum below to show where African Americans were at the end of this phase.

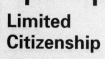

Limited Citizenship

Full Citizenship

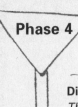

Phase 4

22.5 The End of Reconstruction

Directions: Read Section 22.5 in *History Alive! The United States,* and follow the steps below.

Event Bank:
Ku Klux Klan
Enforcement Acts
Amnesty Act of 1872
Compromise of 1877

FULL CITIZENSHIP

1. Write a short description of each event in the Event Bank that helped African Americans achieve full citizenship.

2. Write a short description of each event in the Event Bank that kept African Americans from achieving full citizenship.

LIMITED CITIZENSHIP

3. Review the items in the Event Bank. Next to each event, write plusses (+) or minuses (–) to show how many steps toward or away from full citizenship African Americans took during this event.

one + or – : minor step forward or back
two + + or – – : medium step forward or back
three + + + or – – – : major step forward or back

4. When directed, draw an X on the spectrum below to show where African Americans were at the end of this phase.

Limited Citizenship   **Full Citizenship**

Phase 5

22.6 Reconstruction Reversed

Directions: Read Section 22.6 in *History Alive! The United States,* and follow the steps below.

Event Bank:
poll tax
literacy tests
Jim Crow laws
Plessy v. Ferguson

1. Write a short description of each event in the Event Bank that helped African Americans achieve full citizenship.

FULL CITIZENSHIP

2. Write a short description of each event in the Event Bank that kept African Americans from achieving full citizenship.

LIMITED CITIZENSHIP

3 Review the items in the Event Bank. Next to each event, write plusses (+) or minuses (–) to show how many steps toward or away from full citizenship African Americans took during this event.

one + or – : minor step forward or back
two + + or – – : medium step forward or back
three + + + or – – – : major step forward or back

4. When directed, draw an X on the spectrum below to show where African Americans were at the end of this phase.

Limited Citizenship

Full Citizenship

PROCESSING 22

Directions: In the space below, use your Reading Notes to create an illustrated road entitled "Road to Full Citizenship." Your road should

- begin with "Limited Citizenship" and end with "Full Citizenship."
- show the progress and setbacks African Americans experienced in their struggle for full citizenship during Reconstruction. For example, hills, twists, and turns away from full citizenship can show setbacks, while straight paths and bridges can show progress.
- include symbols, visuals, and labels for at least two events from each phase of Reconstruction. Stop signs, potholes, and roadblocks might show events that prevented progress toward full citizenship. High speed-limit signs or freeway signs might show events that helped African Americans to achieve their goals.
- show whether you think African Americans reached their goal of full citizenship during Reconstruction.
- be colorful and free from spelling errors.

Credits

Lesson 18
123, Library of Congress